THE IDENTITY OF MAN

The Natural History Press, publisher for The American Museum of Natural History, is a division of Doubleday & Company, Inc. Directed by a joint editorial board made up of members of the staff of both the Museum and Doubleday, the Natural History Press publishes books and periodicals in all branches of the life and earth sciences, including anthropology and astronomy. The Natural History Press has its editorial offices at The American Museum of Natural History, Central Park West at 79th Street, New York 24, New York, and its business offices at 501 Franklin Avenue, Garden City, New York.

THE IDENTITY
OF MAN

—————— ✠ ——————

J. Bronowski

(N̄P)

Published for
The American Museum of Natural History

The Natural History Press
Garden City, New York
1965

CONTENTS

PREFACE

The four essays which follow owe their origin to The American Museum of Natural History, which invited me to inaugurate its newly founded series of lectures on *Man and Nature*. The essays were first given as four lectures at the Museum in New York on 8, 10, 15 and 17 March 1965. Their publication now gives me the opportunity to record my sense of the honor that the Museum did me, and my gratitude for the occasion that it gave me. To these I add my thanks to the Salk Institute for giving me the scholarly setting in which I could develop my subject, and to my biological colleagues there for helping to argue and to shape it.

In one way, these essays begin from and enlarge a theme that I first broached twelve years earlier. In 1953 the Massachusetts Institute of Technology had asked me to examine the human content of science in a series of lectures which have since been published under the title *Science and Human Values*. I came to two radical conclusions there. One was, that the act of discovery in science engages the imagination (first of the man who makes it, and then of the man who appreciates it) as truly as does the act of creation in the arts. The other was, that though the findings of science are, of course, ethically neutral, the activity of science is not: it demands that those who practice it form and hold to a strict set of human values.

These conclusions have since been widely conceded, and I have found nothing in them that I should want to change. Nevertheless, as I have reflected on them in the years that have passed, I have become aware that there remains something to be added to each of them. There is something more to be said about the imagination than that it is alike in science and in the arts. What are the fields over which the imaginative mind ranges in these two pursuits, and what does it bring back from them? Can what we learn from the arts be called knowledge, as what we learn from science can? And if so, what are the two modes of knowledge?

And there is something more to be said about the human values than that science cannot exist without some of them, and must of itself generate these in any society in which it does not find them. What are the values which the arts generate? And where do these two sets of values overlap? These questions prompted me to write in a new preface to *Science and Human Values* in 1961:

> In only one respect would I want to enlarge what I have said here about science and human values, if I were starting afresh today to write about their relation for the first time. In the book as I have written it I have deliberately confined myself to establishing one central proposition: that the practice of science compels the practitioner to form for himself a fundamental set of universal values. I have not suggested that this set embraces all the human values; I was sure when I wrote that it did not; but at the time I did not want to blur the argument by discussing the whole spectrum of values. Now that the crux of my argument has been accepted, I would, were I beginning again, give some space also to a discussion of those values which are not generated by the practice of science—the values of tenderness, of kindliness, of human intimacy and love. These form a different domain from the sharp and, as it were, Old Testament virtues which science produces, but of course they do not negate the values of science. I

shall hope to write about the relation between the two sets of values at another time, and to show how we need to link them in our behaviour.

I made a beginning in that resolve on 17 February 1963 when I gave the substance of the third essay, *Knowledge of the Self,* at the American Academy of Arts and Sciences. When then I landed in New York on a lowering January day in 1964 and found waiting for me the invitation to give these lectures, I read it as an omen and a welcome. What I had written before had been in defense of science. Since then, the defense had won its case. It was now possible, and the time was here, to look beyond that argument at the whole range of the mind as one: the single identity of man. That is the theme that I had long carried about with me, and that these essays set out to present.

J.B.

The Salk Institute for Biological Studies
San Diego, California
1965

One

✠

A MACHINE OR A SELF?

The title of this essay asks a question which is crucial to an inquiry into the identity of man. I take as the starting point for an answer, and for my inquiry, an equally crucial and basic proposition. My fundamental assumption at the outset of these essays is that man is a part of nature.

This simple proposition seems innocent enough, and neutral. Nearly all educated men accept it now: the Bible readers as well as the agnostics, the Sunday strollers and the earnest haunters of museums. In the latter half of the twentieth century, it seems self-evident to say that man is a part of nature, in the same sense that a stone is, or a cactus, or a camel. How easily, indeed, these three childhood categories rise to our lips from *Animal, Vegetable or Mineral* to exhaust the universe. Yet this bland proposition contains the explosive charge which in this century has split open the self-assurance of western man.

For to assert that man is a part of nature surely denies (or seems to deny) that he is unique. This is the hidden charge that troubles yet silences us; it is the perpetual heresy, for which men went to the stake at least as long ago as 1600. Giordano Bruno was asked then to abjure, and would not, his wild belief that the earth we stand on is not the only world, and that we are not the only chosen creatures in the multitude of worlds. This was a piece of Renaissance extravagance that was happy to have man play neither the master nor slave of fate, but simply play in the boundless plenty of nature, and to set both of them free together. But it did not, and still does not, win over the jealous man who wants to guard the sense of his immortal station. He wants to feel that he was cast from birth in a supernatural mold: larger than life, or at least larger than nature.

Thus the statement that man is a part of nature, *Animal, Vegetable or Mineral,* still carries its perpetual heresy, though that has changed its form from century to century. There have been three memorable forms in history, which were in their day not merely religious but intellectual heresies, and outraged revelation and common sense together. Two of these heresies are now so familiar that they offend no one; they were fought for and established by the giants of science, and I need not do more than recall them with a glance. The third gnaws at us still, and makes the subject of this essay and, in the end, of this book.

The first heresy was Bruno's, that our world is not exceptional: whatever exists in the universe is made of the same matter everywhere. The followers of Aristotle did not think so. They thought that the starry heavens are filled with something else and finer than earthly matter— a fifth element, the quintessence; and the Church had made this pagan picture a part of Christian faith. This belief was broken when Galileo broke the crystal spheres by tracing the sunspots and the hills on the moon, and in 1610 by observing that Jupiter has moons which run round it like a clockwork (and Galileo proposed to use them for a clock). Step by step, the laws of earthly mechanics came to command the sky, until it could not be doubted that the star is one with the stone: *Mineral.*

The second heresy attacked the other flank of *Animal, Vegetable or Mineral:* it asserted that man is not unique because he falls into the first category. Specifically, it claimed that man has evolved from a common stock to which other living animals can also be traced back. This heresy was documented in such detail by Charles Darwin in 1859, and championed by Thomas Huxley with such force thereafter, that it has equally become an educated commonplace. None of us doubts that the answer to a question about man begins with *Animal.*

2

The scene, then, is set for the last act in the smoothing out: we sense that there is no break in the continuity of nature. At one end of her range, the star has been linked with the stone; and at the other end, man has been put among the animals. What now remains is between these ends to make a single chain of *Animal, Vegetable or Mineral,* along which nature becomes one with her creatures. An unbroken line runs from the stone to the cactus and on to the camel, and there is no supernatural leap in it. No special act of creation, no spark of life was needed to turn dead matter into living things. The same atoms compose them both, arranged only in a different architecture. This is the third and modern form of the perpetual heresy.

Lest I seem to have overworked the word *heresy,* I will quote chapter and verse. The belief that there is no difference in kind between dead matter and living was uttered to a hushed and shaken public by John Tyndall when he was president of the British Association for the Advancement of Science at Belfast in 1874. Tyndall granted that he had no experimental evidence, and indeed that he could not picture the step from dead atoms to their living arrangement. He scrupulously rejected the spurious evidence for spontaneous generation which was then fashionable; he would have no truck with that to support his belief. And yet, he said,

Believing, as I do, in the continuity of nature, I cannot stop abruptly where our microscopes cease to be of use. Here the vision of the mind authoritatively supplements the vision of the eye. By a necessity

engendered and justified by science I cross the
boundary of the experimental evidence, and discern
in that Matter which we, in our ignorance of its
latent powers, and notwithstanding our professed
reverence for its Creator, have hitherto covered with
opprobrium, the promise and potency of all terres-
trial Life.

Four days later, on 23 August 1874, a London merchant
petitioned the Home Secretary to prosecute Tyndall for
blasphemy, under a seventeenth century act.

And Tyndall's blasphemy was not only religious; it outraged many who no longer believed that man had been
given life in a divine act of creation. They also wanted to
feel that life, so tenuous, so delicate, so tender and so
transient, is distinguished from the dust which gave it
birth and to which it returns by some vital spark. To
this day, skeptics and philosophers as well as churchgoers
long to believe that something outside the natural processes of physics is needed to set matter alight and make
it live.

I do not share this anxiety to find a special dispensation beyond the laws of nature to breathe life into some
of the unexpected configurations of atoms. And indeed, I
think this is something of a philosophers' fraud. Certainly
man is wonderful, and so is life; but they are wonderful
in different ways; and it seems to me a poor exchange
for the dignity of man dethroned to take refuge in the
miracle of life. Whatever makes man unique, it is not the
divine spark of life, or the *élan vital* that enraptured
Henri Bergson. Man is above the other animals not because he is alive as they are, but because he has a life
unlike theirs.

3

What is it that troubles us in the assertion that living things are made from the same atoms as dead, and ruled by the same physical laws? We may pretend that our difficulties are intellectual, and that we are merely puzzled how this could come about. But our uneasiness lies deeper. It lies in a feeling that if the dance of atoms in our bodies is not different in kind from the pattern in the star and the stone, then we have suffered some loss of personality: a denial of the mind in our sense of human self. The great Bishop Butler in *The Analogy of Religion* had felt this long ago in 1736, and John Tyndall (who was morbidly fair) punctiliously included in his blasphemous speech a modern version of the bishop's scruples.

> Your atoms are individually without sensation, much more are they without intelligence. May I ask you, then, to try your hand upon this problem. Take your dead hydrogen atoms, your dead oxygen atoms, your dead carbon atoms, your dead nitrogen atoms, your dead phosphorus atoms, and all the other atoms, dead as grains of shot, of which the brain is formed. Imagine them separate and sensationless; observe them running together and forming all imaginable combinations. This, as a purely mechanical process, is *seeable* by the mind. But can you see, or dream, or in any way imagine, how out of that mechanical act, and from these individually dead atoms, sensation, thought, and emotion are to rise? Are you likely to extract Homer out of the rattling of dice, or the Differential Calculus out of the clash of billiard-balls?

Here we are, in one stride, from the most lowly duck-weed, past the cactus and the camel, to the mind of man. This is where the fulcrum of our fears lies: that man as a species, and we as thinking men, will be shown to be no more than a machinery of atoms. We pay lip service to the vital life of the amoeba and the cheese mite; but what we are defending is the human claim to have a complex of will and thoughts and emotions—to have a mind.

The pith of the problem that nags at our self-esteem is there, and is old and yet peculiarly modern. Other ages phrased it differently: they called it the problem of the soul at one time, of free will at another, and the mind-body problem at a third. We live with it today in a new metaphor that we innocently coined to describe the most awesome of the automata of our age. What we ask now is how a man's brain, if it is full of electric networks, can possibly differ from an electronic brain.

In its general form, of course the question is not new. Descartes argued that animals are and men are not machines; and at this very meeting in Belfast in 1874, Thomas Huxley added to his friend Tyndall's troubles by reading a paper *On the Hypothesis that Animals are Automata*—and for good measure stretched the title to include man among the animals. But such general speculations can now be left behind. For the fact is that what we now know about machines gives a new point and exactness to the question, How far is the brain an automatic machine?

I must not go forward to this cold question without a farewell to Tyndall, who asked it and earned only pulpit thunder and private odium. Poor Alpine hero, he was not prosecuted for blasphemy. Fate lay in wait for him patiently with a more macabre trick. Two years after the Belfast speech, he married a woman twenty-five years younger than he. As time went on, they lived a more and more hidden life in the country. Tyndall dosed himself with the drugs of the day, and one December day in 1893 his wife by mistake gave him a spoonful of chloral which killed him. Yet this was not the last irony. In her remorse, his wife determined to write a worthy biography, in which no detail (she hoarded every scrap that Tyndall had touched) would be out of place. Nothing could be published while she went on pottering; she lived to be ninety-five, and the biography came out five years after her death, in 1945. By then John Tyndall and his scientific work were forgotten.

4

We have to accept the subtle but closely woven evidence that man is not different in kind from other forms of life; that living matter is not different in kind from dead matter; and therefore that a man is an assembly of atoms that obeys natural laws of the same kind that a star does. And this has been brought sharply to a head in the last decade, first by the elucidation of the atomic architecture of the hereditary material in man, and then by recent progress in analyzing the electrical and chemical processes in the brain.

The atoms in the brain as much as those in the body constitute a mechanism, which ticks with the same orderly regularity, and abides by similar laws, as any other interlocking constellation of atoms. Men have uneasily pushed this thought out of their heads because they wanted to avoid the conflict with their rooted conviction that man is a free agent who follows only the promptings of his own will. But we cannot hide this contradiction for ever.

The central theme of these essays is the crisis of confidence which springs from each man's wish to be a mind and a person, in the face of the nagging fear that he is a mechanism. The central question that I ask is: Can man be both a machine and a self?

As I put it, the question is sharply defined. It concerns man and not any other animal; and it concerns his brain and his nervous system, and not all those other bodily functions which he shares quite exactly with other animals. I am not asking about the spark of animal life, but about the working of the human mind.

I think that we are fortunate to have the question put to us thus, as a question about the machinery of mind. For I believe that in this form, the question can be answered; and these essays are meant step by step to construct an answer. In this form, what I shall construct by way of an answer is a philosophy for modern man. I do not mean by that a philosophy which merely makes us comfortable with modern machines. I mean a total philosophy which shows how a man thinks and feels, how he makes his values, what man is—which integrates afresh the experiences which always have been and are human. And on this we can ground a contemporary ethic which is of a piece, because it does not divide the identity of man into the unworthy and the worthy, the irresponsible and the responsible: into machine and self. What is modern about this is simply the setting; we have the luck to receive the question when for the first time it can be answered.

It is pointless to aspire to a self unless we have a lucid notion of what we expect the self to be. And equally it makes no sense to assert that some arrangement is or is not a machine, until we have described the sequence of processes that constitute a machine, in the modern sense. These two definitions, of the self and of a machine, are crucial to these essays. But they are definitions of quite different kinds, which we must be willing now to pursue patiently.

5

When we ask whether man can be more than a machine, we are no longer speaking about mankind at large. It is not man that seeks a self, but each man; I want to be a self, and you do, and we want to be different selves. We think of mankind as a species, the human genotype, only as the faceless skeleton on whose bones our individual differences are molded. We are not asking for a universal self, but for our selves. I want to be a self, and you want to be another; we want our selves to be distinguishable; neither of us wants to be a duplicate copy of the other. Whether we are machines or not, we certainly do not want to be machine *copies*.

So it is pertinent to ask at the outset whether it is possible for all the men now living to be machines, and yet to be different as machines. Could we all be assembled from a strictly limited store of body chemicals, as it were from variants of the basic parts that make up the genotype, and yet no two of us be alike? The answer to this question is Yes. There are enough variants among the body chemicals for each man to be a unique selection from them. We know this because we know that the body tolerates only its own selected set, and rejects all others; and this could not be so if the other selections were not different and (to the body) recognizably different.

Simply as a biological engine, each man can distinguish sharply between his own set of proteins and the next man's. For example, if I scar my face and want to repair it, I must use for the patch a piece of skin from myself (or an identical twin self). It does not matter from what part of my body I take the skin: it will be accepted by my face as mine even if it comes from my back. But if I graft a piece of your skin on my face, it will be rejected, even if it comes from the same place on

your face. My body chemicals can make another face, but
not by matching faces—by matching me; and you are not
me. As chemical engines, we are distinct and incompatible.

Biologists have found these actions so intriguing (and
important) that they have taken to using the word *self*
to mean the set of my body chemicals, and *not-self* to
mean another set. They say that the self recognizes and
respects itself, and rejects what is not-self. These are attractive figures of speech, but they are wide of my meaning, for several reasons.

First, the self so defined is not especially human. All
animals that have climbed to any height on the ladder
of evolution use the same machinery as man does to fight
off invasion of the body. That is, roughly all animals with
a backbone scan the chemical signals of the invader and
use them to evoke a chemical defense—they make anti-
bodies to neutralize the invading proteins. Animals without a backbone do not. This line divides the animal
kingdom neatly somewhere between the hagfish and the
lamprey, of all places—and that surely tells us nothing
about the self in the sense of these essays.

Second, the self in the chemical sense is not unique.
Identical selves happen, and they happen regularly; for
identical twins are such selves which, for example,
accept grafts from one another. And it would beg all
questions about the human self to deny on principle a
separate self to a separate person. The Siamese twins
—who are reported to have shared the same bloodstream
—were markedly different as persons, and the Dionne
quintuplets are. Men want to be selves, that is, different
selves; and they want to be different selves even if they
are identical twins.

And of course, the twins are right. It is a fallacy (the
perpetual fallacy) to suppose that in order to be unique,
one must be born unique. The heresies tried and failed
to unseat just this fallacy: the assumption that man or

life, if they are to be unique, must be endowed with uniqueness as if it were a physical gift, from conception.

6

In order to be unique, it is not necessary to be born unique. Even a machine can become unique; indeed, every machine does. I recognize my own car among all others of the same make by a dozen oddities; the very noise that it makes is individual, and I detect and am alarmed by a change in it at once. The typewriter that Alger Hiss is said to have used was one of thousands like it, yet what it typed was said to be as telltale as his handwriting. In short, a machine acquires an individuality, as I do. Its action today deepens some groove, or wears away some part, which will not be the same again: so that its action tomorrow carries the imprint of today. Even a machine learns and ages; and these two contrary experiences modify its future actions as they do mine.

Nevertheless, we feel that this is not enough to make a self. Certainly we see that a machine changes; that in the process of change, no two machines remain identical; and that, in this sense, each acquires a character of its own, as my car has done. Yet none of us is content to qualify as a self on the ground that, like my car, he makes a peculiar noise when he is running. None of us believes that Alger Hiss's handwriting was given its character wholly by forces of the same kind that aged his typewriter.

When a man says that he is a self, he does indeed mean that his manner is peculiar to him, and that his actions are characteristic: they characterize him, and make him a character. But he does not say all that of himself in the sense in which he says it of an old hat or a motor car. For he believes that the behavior of the hat and the car is predictable, and in that sense is passive.

And he aspires to a self exactly because he does not want to be passive; he believes that his actions have a characteristic logic that is his and is not predictable. He does not merely want to be unique, a different self from you and me: he wants to be a riddle that no one else can read. This is why he will not take the set of his body chemicals for a definition of self, or any other law-abiding machinery. And this is why equally he will not accept his character as a gift from the eccentric but mechanical experiences that rough wear and ill usage stamp on all things: because such a definition does not free the self from the long arm of natural laws.

7

I have been beating the bounds, as it were, along one edge of the definition of self: that which demands that the self shall not be an automaton. This demand, I have shown, is not to be outflanked by any ingenious manipulation of the word *automaton*. It will not do to define the self by its chemical machinery, individual as that usually is; and it will not do, even when we stress the changes which time will work in every machine. These deft devices make the laws which an automaton obeys more elaborate, but they do not change its nature, which is to be law-abiding: they do not turn it from a passive into an active being. In particular, they do not explain the ability of man to break out of the compulsion of instinct and appetite and social ritual in which nature has imprisoned every other animal.

These objections carry us to the other edge of the definition of self. A man does not want to be law-abiding; very well, then it is time to ask him the rude but searching question, Do you want to be lawless? You refuse to be predictable as an engine is, or an animal; do you aspire to be unpredictable? And if so, are you unpredictable to yourself, the actor, as well as to me, the spectator? Do you base your claim to be a self on the proud assertion that your actions are arbitrary?

It is possible to answer Yes to all these questions. This is the central doctrine of existentialism, which holds that only so do we justify our claim to live and not merely to be. We exist only in our actions, says this philosophy, and we prove our existence (above all, to ourselves) by choosing our actions for ourselves. And our actions are only demonstrably our own if they disregard whatever is expected. We show that we are human, that is, that we are free, when we do something that no one can predict. The existentialist proves his existence by an *acte gratuit* which runs counter to the constraints of nature—animal, social and mineral.

It cannot be expected that I, who regard nature not as a constraint but an adventure, will be in sympathy with this philosophy. It is to my mind an extravagant self-assertion by men who have lost the sense of unity with the world, the happy passion which fires the scientist and the painter and the seaside holidaymaker. To me, therefore, existentialism is not an acceptable philosophy, as a matter of taste; and as a matter of fact, I do not think that it is a tenable philosophy. Indeed, we need not argue the matter of taste, for plainly existentialism is not a realistic prescription for anyone's conduct, in fact. No man can hope to behave arbitrarily at every instant, and to conjure round him a constant snowstorm of *actes gratuits*. Neither you nor I can hope to be a self in this sense; and we have therefore still to ask what sense of self we seek.

When I say that I want to be myself, I mean as the existentialist does that I want to be *free* to be myself. This implies that I too want to be rid of constraints (inner as well as outward constraints) in order to act in unexpected ways. Yet I do not mean that I want to act either at random or unpredictably. It is not in these senses that I want to be free, but in the sense that I want to be allowed to be different from others. I want to follow my own way—but I want it to be a way, recognizably my own, and not a zig-zag. And I want people to recognize it: I want them to say, 'How characteristic!'

Of course, if every action of mine were characteristic, then I would be a 'character' but not a self. That is, my actions would be predictable at every moment, once for all, and then I would be a machine (in the eyes of an informed onlooker). But equally, at the opposite extreme, to demand that every action shall be unpredictable also destroys the concept of self. For if I am quite unpredictable, then I am simply a page from a book of random numbers; and that is just as impersonal as a machine. This is not what we mean by a self. A self must have some consistency; its actions tomorrow must be recognizably of a piece with the actions which it carried out yesterday. Spinoza said that three hundred years ago, in effect, and found in it his own impersonal ground for reconciling free will with determinism.

I recall Spinoza not for the form of his resolution (which is too rigid to satisfy us) but for its method. He saw that a man must be defined so that his actions both flow from and flow into his character. Spinoza did not seek such a definition in practical detail because he was preoccupied with the total harmony of nature. Like other philosophers of his century, he took too large and too static a view of the checkered lifetime of a man's behavior. But he did see what we now see, that a man cannot buy his existence, he cannot buy his self, at the price of his coherence.

8

If we are to be more practical than Spinoza, we must seek the sense of self in the precise detail of behavior.

What is it that makes, not the totality of my acts, but some single act, mine and not another's? More important, what makes me aware that it is mine and no one else's; and that it somehow expresses and contains in its detail the lifelong growing totality of me?

This is a question which involves me and my environment together. I act as I do now, I turn the page or pull out my handkerchief, in response to my environment (including my inner environment). If this environment were to repeat itself tomorrow, if I were to come to the bottom of the same page, or feel the same rising sneeze, would I repeat the same gesture? Would I turn the page or flick my handkerchief with the same flourish on the second occasion?

It is sometimes said that quantum physics has answered this question by denying its premise: we now know that it is overwhelmingly improbable that the environment will repeat itself exactly. But this rider, in this context, is neither new nor pertinent; Heraclitus said much this, over two thousand years ago. The events that modify the setting for my actions are part of my experience, and they are so, whether they are gross changes or quantum changes. This is not the crux of the matter.

The crux of the matter is that the second occasion on which I act is different from the first, not by chance but by necessity. However similar it may be in all other ways, it is different because it is a later occasion. What I do tomorrow will have behind it more experience than I have today; in particular, it will have behind it my experience of having already pulled out my handkerchief once before. My flourish the second time is made by a self which is in some way larger than the self that blew his nose the last time.

This conclusion also is not affected by another and deeper implication of quantum physics, which says that the same environment need not yield a unique flourish:

it may touch off any one of a range of flourishes. For experience will still make the second occasion on which I act different from the first, and will thereby shift the range of my possible flourishes. The argument does not depend on the uniqueness of my action, on either occasion, but on the uniqueness of my experience between them.

In short, I am not a fixed character, for I am constantly enlarged by my own experiences. Any definition of the self must allow for this enlargement. The nature of the self derives from the way in which it turns experience into knowledge—that is, into readiness for action.

This is a radical conclusion. The self is not something fixed inside my head. If it exists at all, my self is a process: the unending process by which I turn new experience into knowledge. Once the experience is accepted, digested, and stored in the memory, the machine takes over. From that moment, if I have no new experience, I am in the grip of configurations that are unalterable. In this sense, the brain is a machine; and all vitalist attempts to find the spark of life there are pointless. The dance of atoms, the replication of nucleic acids, the division of cells, the flickering of the nervous system—all that is a machinery and cannot be otherwise. Once an experience has been decisively closed, that machinery is inexorable; and we cannot hope to raise man to selfhood by putting our hand into the works at that stage.

Therefore I hold that a definition of self hinges on the study of human experience. Man has a richer life of experience than the other animals, because his mind alone works consistently with images, and thereby endows him with (literally) a life of imagination. Like a chessplayer, he fears and plans many moves that are not played, they make the footnotes to the game; though not seen, and they belong to the game as much as those that are. In recall, in fantasy, in speculation, and in foresight, man has experiences which do not happen—that is, which are not outward events. And the self is the process in which all his experiences, of the body and of the mind, are fixed as knowledge. What makes man unique is the nature of his knowledge: this is my theme. My analysis of the self is an exploration of human knowledge, and these essays are studies in epistemology.

9

We must now turn to the counterpart of the discussion of self, and ask how we define a machine. At first sight, this seems very simple: surely we know what a machine does, and roughly how it does it. A button is pushed, a switch is thrown, and with a click the machine goes into procedure Number X—it selects a radio channel, it wraps a loaf of bread, it automatically follows the flight of a missile. Yet this picture is wrong because it is too simple; and from its false lucidity spring all the misunderstandings which dog the debate between man and machine.

Nor is this picture given depth if (as is sometimes proposed) we allow an element of chance to the machine, by including some device which tunes it unpredictably to one of several channels. For it is still the nature of such devices, including those of quantum physics, that the chances which they generate have a predictable *distribution*. We do not know which radio channel we shall get next, but we know that we shall get (say) the second channel twice as often as the first, and half as often as the third. This does not make the machine different, or more human, in any essential.

What is wrong is that the picture still describes an old-fashioned machine, which merely obeys mechanical commands. We argue very learnedly about its intestines; but we accept like lambs the naïve notion that the sense organs by which the environment influences it are a set of switches. The poverty of traditional philosophy lies here, in supposing that the outside world pushes the five buttons of our senses, and then free will and determinism have to fight their battle inside the black box that is us.

Our new knowledge of mechanisms goes deeper than this. In the age of the computers, we understand that a machine is not only mechanical on the inside. A machine has an input, a process, and an output, and all three of these must be mechanized. Of course, the old-fashioned sewing machine and the circular saw and the printing press also obeyed a mechanical input and gave a mechanical output. But they had no control over either; input and output were essentially invariant, and we missed their importance. We used to push a button and think that this was the essence of mechanization.

A machine is not merely a whirring train of gears or a humming set of electric circuits. These happy, busy strings of hardware are only the middle step, the visible link, in a procedure which has three steps, and to which the other two are as integral as this is. The machine is the procedure, and the whole procedure, all three steps of it. The first step is the instruction or input, which is the modern form of the button that starts the machine: and which must itself be precise and mechanical, an unequivocal set of holes or marks on a tape that directs the machine into one branch of its network of possible paths. Then comes the physical machinery which obediently carries out the instructions and turns them into actions. And the third step is the result or output, which is equally decisive and definite: in a computer, it is another set of holes or marks on a tape.

It is of cardinal importance here, and essential to my description, that the output from a machine must be exact and unambiguous as the input is. For a modern machine, like a man, is asked in part to regulate itself, and for this purpose it must be able to instruct itself. Such a machine, or a man, must be able to feed its output back

into itself as a new instruction. Its output must therefore be as sharp, within the tolerance of the machine,
as capable of symbolic expression, as well defined and
as single-minded as its input.

10

This is the ground on which I said early in this essay that
we now have the means, for the first time, to look realis-
tically at the machinery of mind. There are, of course,
many mechanical processes in the body and the brain of
men and animals which are old-fashioned machines that
have always been understood. No modern gloss was
needed to explain that alcohol makes you tipsy, or that
the monomania of what Alexander Pope called a master
passion can drive you like a clockwork. A thrush sits on a
cuckoo's egg because it is large; a newly hatched duck-
ling follows the first creature he sees (like the lovers in
A Midsummer Night's Dream) because it moves. Even
in the subtler processes which regulate the equilibrium
of the body and the brain, the spark of life works pretty
mechanically, like any other spark plug; and if it does
not, it goes out. If we did not breathe as simply as an
iron lung, we would die. If we did not hold our tem-
perature steady, like a thermostat, the soul would soon
spurt out of the top of the thermometer with the mercury. If we did not squeeze out the hormones like tooth-
paste there would be no lyric poetry.

All this was understood long ago; Thomas Hobbes
said it at the beginning of *Leviathan* in 1651.

> Seeing life is but a motion of limbs, the beginning
> whereof is in some principal part within; why may
> we not say, that all *automata* (engines that move
> themselves by springs and wheels as doth a watch)
> have an artificial life? For what is the *heart*, but a

spring; and the *nerves,* but so many *strings;* and the *joints,* but so many *wheels,* giving motion to the whole body, such as was intended by the artificer?

But we now understand also that this describes only a primitive kind of machine; and man is not a primitive kind. He is at least as sophisticated as a computer and, like a computer, he is described by the special qualities of his output. If his output can be recorded unequivocally on a tape, he is working like a computer. If it cannot, then he is more sophisticated than a computer.

A computer does not work by being pushed, pulled, moved by a treadle, or fed with any other fixed input. It is mechanical yet flexible at all stages: in its inner workings, and also in the instructions which it accepts and in the output which it may turn into fresh instructions. The essence of the computer, and of all machines, is that the input and the output are also mechanized. If the instructions (including those that may flow from the output) can be put on a tape, we have a machine. If what we have inside us is not to be a machine, it must be because we cannot put and store some of our own instructions to it unequivocally on a tape.

11

In order to see if there is a self in man which is not mechanical, we have to look not inside the brain, but into his acts of experience. We have to analyze the nature of different experiences, and how they are turned into knowledge. This is critical, because once the knowledge is decisively fixed for action, the biological machine must take over. The burden of these essays is the study of two modes of experience, and the knowledge that we derive from them.

I shall show that man is a self in some of his actions

because his procedures for getting experience cannot all be formalized. The messages from the outside world and his inner world together do not all strike him like holes punched in a tape, or magnetic marks made on it. The total of his sense impressions, his stored reflections from the past, and the interplay of thought between them, includes a mode of knowledge that cannot be written out in symbols as the new input for a machine.

I am asserting that there is a mode of knowledge which cannot be spelled out formally to direct a machine. It may be asked, Any machine? If this is a question in the present, then the answer is Yes. For example, we know (from the work of Kurt Gödel and A. M. Turing) that no machine that uses strict logic can examine its own instructions and prove them consistent. But if it is a question about the measureless future, then it cannot be answered. A machine is not a natural object; it is a human artifact which mimics and exploits our own understanding of nature; and we cannot foresee how radically we may come to change that understanding. We cannot foresee and we cannot conceive all possible machines— if indeed the word *all* has a meaning in this sentence. All that we can say, and all that I can assert, is that we cannot now conceive any kind of law or machine which could formalize the total modes of human knowledge.

As for the modes of knowledge, I have come so far that I must not stop without saying what I mean. I am going to discuss in these essays two ways in which I can decide to flick my handkerchief differently tomorrow than I did today. One way is simple: I summarize it in the resolve, 'I won't make that flourish again because last time it hit my wife.' That is a physical error, and a formal knowledge of Newton's laws will avoid it; thus a machine can be made to appreciate and correct it.

But there is also another sort of resolve which says, 'I won't make that flourish again because last time it embarrassed my wife.' That resolve is based on a different mode of knowledge which is not formal, yet which (I hold) has an equal place in our minds. I call this mode, knowledge of the self; for it requires that I recognize myself in my wife, and what I learn thereby illuminates my self and hers together. There is nothing in the actions of machines to match this recognition, which is real and powerful in human affairs. Charles Darwin said of himself with regret, 'My mind seems to have become a kind of machine'; yet it was this other mode of knowledge which caused him to leave the *Origin of Species* unpublished for twenty years, in part at least because he knew that it would embarrass his wife.

Two

✠

THE MACHINERY
OF NATURE

In my first essay, I posed the question which is central to my theme: Is man a machine or a self? My conclusion in that essay was that the answer will hinge on the possible modes of knowledge: that is, on how we turn experience into self. If all knowledge can be formalized, then the human self can be matched, in principle, by a machine.

But it is possible to seek a more active meaning in the word *self:* that is, in the idea that we have of what makes each of us a person. The traditional ideas are out of date because they picture the person as something given and static, a thing; and that inevitably makes him a mechanism. We have to conceive the human self quite differently. The self constantly grows and changes as it has new experiences, and what characterizes it are its modes of turning experience into itself and into knowledge. We shall find the character of the self by studying the two distinct ways in which it gets knowledge.

The mode that I study in this essay is science, that is, knowledge of the physical working of the world. Some scientists shy from the word *knowledge,* and insist that they do no more than discover operations that are effective in controlling nature. I do not think that this distinction means much. Indeed, I do not think that knowledge has the abstract qualities that would allow us to draw such a distinction. My view is that knowledge is a rearrangement of experience, in which we put together those experiences that seem to us to belong together, and put them apart from those that do not. And the control of nature depends on just this separation, between actions that have been shown to be relevant to a given end, and those that appear irrelevant. A scientific theory, and the whole scientific picture of the world, is an imaginative grouping of all these experiences. But this does not make it less practical. In my view, it is not possible to act practically without forming a picture of the world by implication, as an integral part of our action. We do not operate on nature by fits and starts, but by forming our experiences into a connected view.

I shall draw such a picture of the world in outline, and sketch the machinery of nature as we conceive it now. My aim is then to show the processes of the mind by which men have arrived at this scientific description. The sequence of theories that I have chosen to present is directed to this aim, which is to discover the ground both for empirical and for logical reasoning in science.

2

The physical properties of the world seem to us now to be explained most vividly and consistently if we think of them as flowing from the to and fro of large numbers of separate particles. The particles that underlie the everyday world are molecules: most physical processes are exchanges between small molecules, and most biological processes are exchanges between large molecules. These processes also exchange energy, which is also particulate or grainy; oddly, the physical processes usually exchange large numbers of energy quanta, and the biological processes usually exchange small numbers.

The molecules are themselves cooperative assemblies of atoms—a few atoms at a time in physics, several thousand atoms at a time in biology. And the atoms in their turn are assemblies of still smaller fundamental particles: electrons, protons, and neutrons. Thus the architecture of nature is built up, step by step, always from stable assemblies of smaller particles. What characterizes an assembly—what distinguishes one kind of molecule from another, for example, and one species of atom from another—is as much its geometry as the particles that go to make it.

This single and unitary picture of the world explains, simply and delightfully, all the daily behavior of matter. Why does glue stick? How does a pencil write? How does the electric light work? Why do we see the flash of lightning before we hear the thunder? How does a detergent get at the dirt? Why is ice smooth? Why does it melt when it gets hot? Why do we blow on the soup? John Tyndall asked why the sky looks blue, and gave the answer in a heavenly phrase: 'because we live *in* the sky, not under it.' When I had to measure the flash from the atomic bombs in Japan, I asked why granite suddenly roughens when it gets very hot. The answer (which has to do with the crystal structure of quartz) turned out to be as practical—and as beautiful, in its revelation of the geometry of nature.

3

All these questions, whose slow elucidation is a pleasure and a wonder of childhood, the atomic picture of the world answers. And for our generation, there have been added the pleasure and the wonder of adult learning. For the atomic picture has been shown, and shown for the first time to us who are alive now, to give a profound coherence also to the hidden processes of nature. It justifies the perpetual heresy in unexpected depth. For example, we now see that matter in the stars is indeed like ours, but is our matter in evolution. Helium is formed by the collision of hydrogen atoms, carbon by the rare collision of helium atoms, and there are similar changes up the atomic scale. The stars are stepping-stones in cos-

mic history, along which the atoms, like species, move
from simple to complex.

Yet more remarkable than this finding is the discovery
that the atomic machinery works as concretely in the cells
as in the stars; it makes physical sense of the processes in
the living body. We see now that life reproduces itself
by means of long molecules which can copy themselves.
We understand how these molecules work as tapes of
instructions in the hereditary part of the cell, and (rather
less well) how they work in the rest of it. We know the
alphabet of four stable assemblies, made for the most
part from atoms of carbon, nitrogen, hydrogen, and oxy-
gen, which spells out these long molecules. We shall soon
know how the twenty basic words in the vocabulary of
the cell, the amino-acids, are spelled by triplets from this
four-letter alphabet. We know something, but less, about
the machinery which causes cells to specialize. And we
know least about the way in which the specialized cells
cooperate to make those vast and integrated colonies of
cells that we call you and me—the living creatures.

Beyond this knowledge, new, exhilarating, and still
thin, lies a larger field of ignorance, the brain. The brain
is a part of the central nervous system, and it is not a
homogeneous part; for example, some of its layers came
into being later than others in the evolution of man. In
one sense, the brain is more like a manmade machine
than is the rest of the body. I mean by this that the child
is born with most of the cells in the brain already formed
—this is why his head is so charmingly and dispropor-
tionately large, almost one quarter of his height. From
time to time during life, some of the cells die off but,
unlike cells in the body, they are not replaced. The
machinery of the brain does not mend itself, and by the
end of life it may lack, at a guess, one out of every ten
cells that it started with. We presume that the design of
the brain has allowed for this loss in advance by building

in a great deal of redundancy, that is, of alternative ways to handle the same message.

4

It used to be said, in a classical phrase, that the brain is a telephone exchange. That is, it was thought that information from the senses reaches the brain piecemeal, in single and neutral signals, and that these are then sorted out and interpreted by logical processes which derive messages for action from them. The most striking new knowledge that we have about the brain is that this analogy is wrong, and must be wrong. At one end, the brain does not receive a neutral input from the senses. And at the other end, it does not form its output by the kind of logical reasoning that we understand.

By way of caution, I ought first to say that there are indeed some simple circuits in the brain that do work like a telephone answering service. For example, there are the remarkable centers which James Olds discovered in 1953; when they are stimulated, the animal feels direct pleasure. The pleasure is so great and so lasting that a hungry animal will constantly prefer it to food if it is given the choice. Close to these centers for pleasure, there are also centers for pain in the brain, whose response is as immediate and as powerful.

But these direct and, as it were, classical circuits (most pleasure and pain centers lie in the older brain) are not the rule. As a rule, signals that carry information to the brain or instructions from it take many steps, and are checked back and balanced and intertwined along the nervous system many times. Our senses doctor their messages before they reach the brain: for example, the sense of sight does so.

A series of searching and delicate experiments has

shown in the last years that the eye does not send blank
and unbiased signals to be interpreted in the brain. H. K.
Hartline and later workers have studied the sense of
sight in several species of animals. They have found that
the rods and cones in the retina are connected together
in complex groups, and groups of groups, within the eye.
The number of cross-links is huge, and their business is
to integrate the individual sensations before they leave
the eye. The eye does not respond to this single flash or
that. It tries from the outset to find a pattern in what it
sees, and the pattern it looks for is the shape of things.
For example, the inner connections in the cat's eye make
it sensitive to sharp edges. The frog's eye is more sensitive to edges if they are moving, and to quickly changing or moving contrasts of light and shade.

Thus the message which the cat's and the frog's eye
sends back to the brain, and our eye too, is not an array
of dark and light dots like a television tube, but is already a parcel that outlines a bounded and moving
shape—a thing. A single nerve fiber does not say to the
brain, 'My part of the field of vision is dark'; it says 'The
edge of something is crossing it'. The single fiber takes
note of what is going on all around a point in its field; it
does not send a report from the point that by itself is
meaningless; it signals a meaningful piece of a shape.

And the single fiber is imperious; often, it does not so
much inform the brain as instruct it, by sorting its messages in advance; and it does this most effectively by
simply withholding information—by judging for itself
what is irrelevant, and discarding it, without leave from
the brain. This is shown in the elegant work of Horace
Barlow on the rabbit. There seem to be preferred directions in the rabbit's eye: it observes up and down
well, and straight across the eye, but not (it seems)
diagonally across. But more unexpected are the preferences not of the eye as a whole, but those built into sin-

gle neurons. One kind of neuron will observe a downward movement and ignore an upward movement; another will do just the opposite. One kind of neuron observes the fast movement of an object and overlooks its slow movement; another does the opposite.

In all these preferences, the rabbit does not *see* better or worse; its eye is equally sharp to see them all; it *observes* better because the connections in the eye are arranged to pick out and respond to the special directions and movements. As an optical instrument, the rabbit's eye is unbiased. But the eye is not only an optical instrument; it is also an electrical network in which each unit integrates the darks and lights that it sees into messages, and decides which message should alert the attention and which need not. When a unit of the electrical network interprets the sequence of darks and lights as a downward movement, it sends back a strong visual message to the brain. But when the movement appears to be upward, this unit censors its message: it records and sends a weak message, or none at all.

It is likely that the units in their turn are grouped to send overall messages which are important to the rabbit. For example, those that detect slow movements probably concentrate on the horizon. And it plainly makes sense in the evolution of the rabbit that it should be more alert to the distant stalker and to the tall looming shape, to some movements than to others, and that it should push its early warning system as far forward as possible, out from the brain into the sense organs. The survival of any animal demands that it shall judge the significance of the shapes and movements that it sees as soon as possible, and we have now discovered that it does that in the senses. But the discovery puts an end to the belief of philosophers that the brain receives a neutral picture of the world and sits in judgment over it. William Blake wrote,

I question not my Corporeal or Vegetative Eye any more than I would Question a Window concerning a Sight. I look thro' it & not with it.

Like everything he wrote, this is vigorous and visionary together; but it is mistaken.

5

At the other end of the chain of command in the brain, we ask how it decides what orders it shall give. It was tempting to think in the past that the orders are worked out from the information by logical steps as in an automatic telephone exchange—or, to make the analogy more pointed, in an electronic computer. But it was shown by John von Neumann just before he died in 1957 that this cannot be so. In a moment, as I write, my brain will tell my hand where to put the dot that closes this sentence. If my brain calculated the many steps in this command as a computer does, then the precision which it reaches in its final instruction to my hand would require each step to be accurate to at least ten decimals. But the electric mechanism which the brain and the central nervous system use cannot work more accurately at any one step (we know by a basic study of its mode of transmission) than three decimals at most. Therefore the brain is at least ten million times too coarse to work by the methods of the manmade computer, and does not reach its decisions by the classical logic that we know. In von Neumann's phrases, it uses a radically different system of notation from the one we are familiar with, namely a system in which the meaning is conveyed by the *statistical* properties of the message. I quote one of the last sentences that John von Neumann wrote:

Logics and mathematics in the central nervous system, when viewed as languages, must structurally be essentially different from those languages to which our common experience refers.

When we reason with pencil and paper, say in the mathematical parts of science, we use a logic of strict certainty. The brain does not use this logic of the large world in its minute inner workings. We do not know what logic it uses, but it cannot be this. Indeed, in trying to wish this logic on to the brain, we are as inverted as those physicists of the past who tried to govern the atom by the principles of engineering. Engines are built up from atoms, not the other way about; and classical logic is built up from the logic of the brain, not the other way about. The brain cannot reach its inner conclusions by any logic of certainty. In place of this, the brain must do two things. It must be content to accept less than certain knowledge. And it must have statistical methods which are different in kind from ours, by which it reaches its acceptable level of uncertainty. By these means, the brain constructs a picture of the world which is less than certain yet highly interlocked in its parts.

I use this phrase designedly: an interlocked picture of the world. We do not know how the brain fixes its picture—for example, how the memory works. But we are in any case mistaken if we think of our picture of the world as a passive record. The picture is made by, it is made of, our activity, all the way from the logic of the brain to the use of the plow and the wheel. It is the implication and the expression, in symbolic form, of all our dealings with nature. The picture is not the look of the world but our way of looking at it: not how the world strikes us but how we construct it. Other people and other ages had different pictures from ours, and that is why incidentally they drew differently. We must not think that those who stitched the Bayeux Tapestry habitually saw in perspective but did not know how to draw in it. No doubt they could see in perspective, as we can manipulate an optical illusion in our heads; but their habit, their total cast of mind, was to look at relations in the world differently, and that is what they drew. A modern story from Margaret Mead makes the point.

This relationship to the physical environment is a kind of *being in* rather than *seeing* the environment. There is a very moving instance of a group of Australian aboriginal children who were incarcerated in a reform school, far away from their own people. One of the custodial staff, who had been a teacher, started the children in crafts and drawing. Suddenly, one day, a little boy shouted, "I see, I see! You don't draw it the way you *know* it is. You draw it the way it looks!" And the idea of perspective was born anew in his mind.

6

From all this I draw a conclusion about the nature of knowledge which seems to me now inevitable. It concerns the procedure by which we reach general statements by reasoning from the particular instances we find strewn about the outside world: the first step in what in science is called induction. This procedure is usually thought to be lodged in the brain alone. But it is evident from what we know now that this is not so. What happens instead is that there is, as it were, a continuous conversation between the brain and the senses. The eye sends back a message which says that it has seen a thing. Its description of the thing is rudimentary; but I will suppose, to sharpen the exposition, that it would fit a zebra. The brain, rummaging about among likelihoods, refuses to acknowledge a zebra in the Arctic. Could it be a polar bear?

it asks. No, says the eye, it jumps and it has stripes. (I am exaggerating the debate to the point of caricature: but just that gives the essence of it.) Then it must be an albino seal, says the brain, matching an imaginative conjunction of oddities out of the categories that it knows. And so the conversation goes on, until the brain is satisfied either that it has, or has made, a niche for the creature among its categories—or dismisses it as a deception. For we must not forget that deception and hallucination are as normal as are sound judgments, and there is nothing different in the procedure which leads to the one or to the other. No generalization is foolproof.

Now that the brain has created a new general category, an albino seal or a trick of the Arctic light, the eye will in future search a wider range of alternatives; there are more messages to pass between it and the brain. And next time that the eye sights what might be an albino seal, the brain will have to take the next step in induction: it will have to guess what law rules its reappearance. Is it the same seal, and if so, what is the law of the migration of seals? Or is it another, and if so, what is the law of the inheritance of albinism? The senses play their part in this debate also. The procedure of induction by which we make—and make rules for—general categories, by which indeed we build up a language of general words, is a constant to and fro between the brain and the senses.

This analysis makes it plain that it is not possible for the brain to arrive at *certain* knowledge. All those formal systems, in mathematics and physics and the philosophy of science, which claim to give foundations for certain truth are surely mistaken. I am tempted to say that we do not look for truth, but for knowledge. But I dislike this form of words, for two reasons. First of all, we do *look* for truth, however we define it; it is what we *find* that is knowledge. And second, what we fail to find is not truth but certainty; the nature of truth is exactly the knowledge that we do find. The only unexpected rider here is that truth, in this sense, has more than one mode; scientific knowledge is only one of its modes. It will be the burden of my next essay to examine the other mode, which is knowledge of self. Scientific knowledge is a stricter mode than this, in a definable sense, but it is not truer: it is not certain. No knowledge can be certain that continues to expand with us as we live inside the growing flesh of our experience.

Our experiences do not merely link us to the outside world; they are us and they are the world for us; they make us part of the world. We get a false picture of the world if we regard it as a set of events that have their own absolute sequence and that we merely watch. And here I am crossing from philosophy into physics. Albert Einstein demonstrated just this as a plain matter of fact in the theory of relativity. If we write the laws of nature as if we ourselves had no part in them, we get the wrong answers to quite elementary questions, for example about the orbit of the planet Mercury. The basic mistake in that calculation springs, Einstein showed, from supposing that nature is an imperturbable machine at which we peek from the outside. That is the false picture, in physics and in philosophy. Nature is a network of happenings that do not unroll like a red carpet into time, but are intertwined between every part of the world; and we are among those parts. In this nexus, we cannot reach certainty because it is not there to be reached; it goes with the wrong model, and the certain answers ironically are the wrong answers. Certainty is a demand that is made by philosophers who contemplate the world from outside; and scientific knowledge is knowledge for action, not contemplation.

7

Plainly, it matters in the most practical way that we rightly understand how we ourselves are embedded in the system of science that we in part discover and in part create. Such a system describes the activity of nature, and ourselves in it; it is not a blueprint of the machinery of nature. We are an active and intimate part of our descriptions of her. Science then is not so much a model of nature as a living language for describing her. It has the structure of a language: a vocabulary, a formal grammar, and a dictionary for translation. The vocabulary of science consists of its concepts, all the way from universal gravity and the neutron to the neuron and the unconscious. The rules of its grammar tell us how to arrange the concepts in sensible sentences—that atoms can capture neutrons, for example, and that heavy atoms when they split will release them. And the dictionary then translates these abstract sentences into practical observations that we can test in the everyday world: for example, in the damage that neutrons do when plutonium is split.

Thus science is a language whose structure mimics the behavior of the world; and when we use it, we acknowledge that we cannot separate ourselves from the behavior we describe, when we need a concept (like gravity) or discard one (like phlogiston). For every language is open, alive and changing; it has to invent new words and to experiment with new usages and thereby discover new meanings in what it can say. When J. J. Thomson discovered the electron in 1897 he added a new word, that is, a new concept to the language of science: a unit of matter smaller than the atom. In showing that what he had found behaved like a particle, he fixed (as it were) the first grammatical rules to govern the use of the new word. A little later, it was discovered that 'When electrons change their speed, they also change their mass'; and that new sentence gave a new usage to the word *mass* which fantastically enlarged the conceptual language of physics. Nor was that the end of the electron; in time, J. J. Thomson's son showed that it could also behave like a wave, and changed the grammar again. A new concept in science is as rich and far-reaching a verbal invention, a marriage of words, as is, say, the word *Blitzkrieg* in the vocabulary of warfare—a massive packing into a single idea of a whole new strategy of organization.

And the new concept is as real, neither more nor less, than the content of the word *Blitzkrieg*. An electron is not a fiction, any more than warfare is, or gravity. They are all real: that is, their behavior is real in the sense that it can be described, its implications are real in the sense that they can be forecast, and its consequences are real in the robust sense that they can be observed. We have the right therefore to say, if we choose, that an electron is a real *thing*—but we would be foolish to exercise that right, because it would place on us the duty to disentangle our use of the word *thing* here from its everyday use. There is no point in kidnaping the word *thing* for a new meaning if we then have to explain that it is not the same as the familiar meaning—and that in effect we do not know what the new meaning is. A fundamental particle such as an electron is real, but it is not a thing like a table, or like any other thing except another fundamental particle. To say this is manifestly the same as saying that nothing is added by calling it a thing. We do best to use it as a natural part of our language in its own right.

Of course we cannot suppose that we know all the properties of the electron, or that they may not turn out to be the partial aspects of some more subtly entwined structure in nature. What we discover in nature is real, in the sense that I have described, but it is surely not the whole or the final description of physical reality. Nature is surely richer, more finely woven and interwoven, and more ingeniously organized within herself than any one of our explanations. Pope Urban VIII insisted that Galileo must end the *Dialogue on the Great World Systems* with this specific caution:

It would be an extravagant boldness for anyone to go about to limit and confine the Divine power and wisdom to some one particular *fantasia* of his own.

In its context, this was a cynical assertion by the Pope that no explanation is to be preferred to any other. In this sense, the assertion is false, and Galileo was rightly reluctant to pay lip service to it. It did not even save him from the Inquisition. Yet in a larger and more generous context, what Urban VIII saw is true. The concepts we create, the laws we find, are fragments in the whole language of nature. The marvel is that we get along so well when we speak so little of her language: when we guess only parts of the vocabulary, and few of the grammatical rules which connect them.

8

I have chosen to describe science as an account of the machinery of nature, not in engineering terms, but in linguistic ones. One persuasive reason is that I shall be talking in the next essay about literature, and whatever I have to say there by way of likeness or of contrast will be said more fairly if I use a common model of language in both places. But a more cogent reason, of course, is that language is a more telling and a better model for science than is any mechanism. We receive experience from nature in a series of messages. From these messages we extract a content of information: that is, we decode the messages in some way. And from this code of information we then make a basic vocabulary of concepts and a basic grammar of laws, which jointly describe the inner organization that nature translates into the happenings and the appearances that we meet.

Somewhere in this decoding, the mind takes a critical step from the individual experience to the general law which embraces it. How do we guess the law and form the concepts that underlie it? How do we decide that there are, and how do we give properties to, such invisible things as atoms? That the atoms in their turn are composed of more fundamental particles? How do we convince ourselves that there is a universal quantity called energy, which is carried by single quanta, yet which spreads from place to place in a motion like a wave? And that the rearrangement of atoms, and still more fundamental particles, consumes or releases energy? How do we come to picture a living process in these dead terms?

Take as a concrete example again the structure of the eye, which Bishop Butler and Henri Bergson both thought too marvelous to be explained by mechanical evolution. After centuries of preparation, how do we come to conclude that the small rods and cones in my retina are sensitive to single quanta of light, that these quanta untwist the molecules of visual purple, that this chemical change is integrated electrically in my eye with others like it and signaled to my brain, and that the coloring of the picture that it evokes there has been fixed at my conception by the same fragments of my father's sperm and my mother's ovum that determined my sex?

I have only to describe this complex, farfetched and intricately connected sequence to make it evident that no simple set of observations will suffice to establish it. In the first place, it is a highly generalized account which could not be derived from single experiments, even at a single point in the sequence. We have to fit together many separate experiments to reach, for example, the plain conclusion that visual purple is bleached, or that this chemical change is signaled as an electric impulse. To say something persuasive about the optic nerve, we need the evidence of a host of other observations on a multitude of other nerves. And when we look beyond one of these generalizations along their whole connected sequence, we realize how they lock and engage with, how they are fixed and held in place by, all the generalizations of physics and chemistry and biology and the physiology of the nervous system.

The most modest research worker at his bench, pushing a probe into a neuron to measure the electric response when a light is flashed, is enmeshed in a huge and intertwined network of theories that he carries into his work from the whole field of science, all the way from Ohm's law to Avogadro's number. He is not alone; he is sustained and held and in some sense imprisoned by the state of scientific theory in every branch. And what he finds is not a single fact either: it adds a thread to the network, ties a knot here and another there, and by these connections at once binds and enlarges the whole system.

This is worth saying, even though it has always been so, because it is still neglected by philosophers. They see that science passes from fact to prediction, from instance to law, by a procedure of generalization—what is usually called induction. To reason in this direction, from the particular to the general, cannot be justified on logical grounds: David Hume showed that more than two hundred years ago. But more incisive than the question, What right have we to form inductions? is the question, How do we form them? Hume gave no explanation of this except habit—

> We are determined by CUSTOM alone to suppose the future conformable to the past

—and philosophers have followed him ever since. Their theories are still dominated by their belief that science is an accumulation of facts, and that a generalization grows of itself from a heaping of single instances in one narrow field. They think that a scientist is persuaded that light arrives at the eye in a shower of quanta because he does an experiment, does it again, and repeats it to be sure.

Alas, this is not at all what any scientist does. He may indeed repeat an experiment two or three times, if its outcome strikes him as odd and unexpected. But even here, he means by odd and unexpected precisely that it conflicts with what other experiments in other fields have led him to believe. The suspicion with which all scientists treat the published evidence for extrasensory perception shows this. A set of results is odd and unexpected, in the end it is unbelievable, because it outrages the intricate network of connections that has been established between known phenomena.

9

The classical error is to regard a scientific law as only a shorthand for its instances. If we think like this, then naturally we can argue only among instances: 'I have seen the sun rise every morning of my life, so I expect it to rise as long as I live'. This is a fair expectation by habit, but it is not an induction; I might as well conclude, 'So I expect to live as long as it rises'. An induction is not a guess at the next instance, and the next, and the next, but at the law which rules and, more deeply, which explains their occurrence.

Indeed, it is a mistake to think of an induction as a forecast, and to be preoccupied with the guess that it makes about the future. An induction in science is a generalization which tries to thread its way through our experience and to guess what law has governed that. We are no more certain of the law in the past than in the future, for no law that we discover is certain and final. But now we are looking for a law, not as a calculating but as a unifying device. In this sense, Mendeleeff's perception in 1869 that the properties of the atoms return in a regular cycle was penetrating; and our expectation that the sun will return regularly is not.

The hope that the law will hold into the future is a separate step; yet even in that step, we think about the law and not about the next instance. To calculate the probability for tomorrow's sunrise, as Pierre Laplace did, is wide of the mark. At bottom, it is an attempt to weigh the evidence for a law that governs the movements of the sun and the earth—but the wrong law. If the sun fails to rise tomorrow, it will be because we were mistaken in our guess at much deeper laws: the planetary and cosmic laws. The criticism of induction with which David Hume shocked scientists in 1739 is not a lament for our habits of prediction, but for our ignorance; the crucial sentence in it is,

The powers, by which bodies operate, are entirely unknown.

Induction in science is the search for, the guess at, the unattainable laws that describe these powers.

A concept is formed, a law is proposed, not because the repetition of an experiment makes it inevitable, but because a crisscross of evidence from many different kinds of experiments supports this hypothesis (and confounds others) as a plausible way of linking them all together. What persuades us are the inner connections, and what we look for is a law from which all the results will flow as related consequences.

There is an infinity of laws any one of which will explain one experiment, however often we repeat it. There still remains an infinity of laws that might explain all the different experiments. Yet the crisscross serves to knock out this and then that hypothesis which is attractive because it is simple, but which turns out to be too simple. The point of adding a new experiment to the crisscross is precisely to cut down the number of adequate explanations that remain. This is the lucid thought of Karl Popper —that the aim of an experiment must always be to overthrow a hypothesis. We design a new experiment to be critical: that is, to be decisive in knocking out one of two alternative simple hypotheses each of which explains the results that we have so far. What we try to reach in this way is the simplest law that will hold together the total complex of our evidence.

10

We cannot hope to match the total complexity of nature any more precisely than a language matches the complexity of social life. The answer to the polite inquiry 'How are you?' is not a medical bulletin. And the answer to the scientific inquiry 'How are atoms of carbon made?' is not a full analysis of the mind of the Almighty. There is a tolerant give and take in the reply that we make to questions about our health; and there is the same give and take, an essential tolerance, in the sentences that we can frame to picture the improbable generation of the carbon atom. A single experiment can be described in a bulletin; but the grand processes of nature cannot be sketched without the ambiguity which dogs all language. Science would come to a standstill if every ambiguity were resolved, for there would be nothing left to discover. It is this which makes it more vivid and more enlightening to call science a language for the machinery of nature and not an engineering drawing.

In this century, it has been the hope of positivist philosophers to make a map of the world like a piece of graph paper, from primitive statements that 'This is a red dot'. The progress of physics has shown that this cannot be done, as a description of reality. And it is now clear that it is not a description of what the senses tell us either.

The sense of sight integrates its sensations before they go to the brain, and its messages carry back information not about dots but about things. Even the signal 'red' (we know from the eye of those monkeys that see colors) cannot be sent without a message about the shape of the thing that evokes it.

I ought to say, of course, that some philosophers of science have disputed the view that I hold, that a concept is an imaginative creation. They have started from the thought that a concept is a shorthand for the facts that fall under it—as in some sense it surely is. And they have gone on to hope that perhaps it might be defined precisely as a shorthand for the facts and nothing more. This is the operational view widely held in America under the influence of Percy Bridgman: length is a sequence of measurings; mass is what you do when you find the mass; an electron is an array of observations and nothing else. A like idea was current in England at least since 1918, when Bertrand Russell wrote,

> The supreme maxim in scientific philosophising is this: *Wherever possible, logical constructions are to be substituted for inferred entities.*

The idea that all scientific concepts are purely logical constructions was held, in this form, by positivist philosophers also. In order to leave no doubt what this view supposed, I will quote a meticulous account of it.

> Electrons, on this view, are logical constructions out of the observed events and objects by which their presence can be detected; this is equivalent to saying that the word 'electron' can be explicitly defined in terms of such observations. Every sentence containing the word 'electron' can, on this view, be translated without loss of meaning into a sentence in which there occur only words which denote entities (events, objects, properties) which are directly ob-

servable. It may be very difficult to make this translation, but it is always possible to do so.

This strictly formal rendering of scientific concepts was shown to be untenable by the young English philosopher Frank Ramsey, who died in 1930 at the age of twenty-six. He saw and demonstrated the shortcomings of the operational and positivist attitude sharply. It is the right attitude in a science which is closed; it is hopelessly the wrong one when a science is still growing. For a logical construction which has been made to contain only the existing facts and relations cannot accommodate new relations. If your definition of mass, say, is operationally or logically exact, then it is too narrow; it leaves you no room to discover that mass is also equivalent to energy. The concepts of a growing science must be richer and more pliable than any logical construction from the sum of its known facts. Ramsey proved this practically by inventing an example in mathematical logic, and simpler examples have since been added by his friend Richard Braithwaite, from whom I have been quoting.

There is no way to avoid some ambiguity in every human language and, in spite of appearances, the language of science is not an exception. The concepts which form the critical words in its vocabulary mean much the same thing to every user, and yet they do not mean quite the same thing. If they did, then no one could begin to think of a fresh relation. Time did not mean the same thing to Albert Einstein that it had meant to physicists before him. Energy did not mean the same thing to Max Planck that it had meant to James Joule, and it had meant more to Joule with his giant thermometers than it had meant to his conventional predecessors. And in our own generation, there has been uncovered in the word *life* a meaning which was hidden to all those who have used it since time immemorial. To us, what Einstein did, what Planck did, what James Watson and Francis Crick have done, appears crudely as a discovery; but to them, it was an elucidation of the language of science which uncovered and sharpened in its conceptual vocabulary a potential of meaning which others had missed. Imagination takes advantage of ambiguity, in the language of science as well as in the language of poetry.

11

We cannot describe the world by an enumeration of its appearance; that is the flaw in any system of scientific philosophy which seeks to get rid of all concepts. There is no descriptive language that does not consist of general words, that is, of concepts. The gift of humanity is precisely that, unlike the animals, we form concepts; and we express that gift in our thinking language. Man constantly invents ideas to express what seems to him to lie behind the appearances of nature and to hold them together. The invention of these ideas and their interplay in language is imagination—the making of images inside our heads. In this sense, science is as much a play of imagination as poetry is. And the language of science cannot be freed from ambiguity, any more than poetry can: ambiguity lies in the very texture of all ideas. In spite of its tidy look, the structure of science is no more exact, in any ultimate and final sense, than that of poetry. The difference between the two languages does not lie there.

Of course it is true that when scientists write out their findings, they try to rid their language of ambiguity and to make it exact. Aldous Huxley in his last book presented that as the crucial difference between the two parts of his title *Literature and Science*. But this confuses the language in which science is invented with that in which it is explained—the thought with its formal communication. Man has outdistanced the other animals because he has not one but two languages: a thinking language for manipulating concepts inside his head, as well as a speaking language (such as animals have) for communicating with others. A scientific discovery is searched for, a law is first guessed at, by the ambiguous processes of induction, and they are carried out in the thinking language. But the exposition of science is not an account of the processes of discovery. On the contrary, its aim is to display the discovery definitively, and place it in the network of axioms and laws, so that everyone can then reason about it unequivocally. It must be so, in order that the consequences of the new discovery may be logically deduced, and tested in specific instances.

The exposition of science is always an instruction for testing the totality of laws as they stand at that moment. It could therefore be put on a tape that would direct a testing machine. This is because the exposition displays the state of science at that moment as a complete and closed system, wholly contained in (that is, deducible from) its axioms and laws. The man who has to act now on present scientific knowledge has to accept that as an instruction, as a machine does. This is the nature of science as a mode of knowledge. It must be testable in action; so that, however it was discovered and however it will be corrected, at any moment it must be formally fixed as a system of instructions. But the thinker and experimenter does not have to accept the present state of science as closed, and its exposition as complete. He is free to work in the thinking language, and to explore its ambiguities to his mind's content.

Science is a different pursuit from poetry not in its execution but in its endeavor. For the endeavor of science is to resolve ambiguities by making what I have described as critical and decisive tests between alternatives. An experiment to this end is as beautiful and as imaginative as any line of poetry, but it puts its imagination to a different endeavor: unlike poetry, it does not seek to exploit its ambiguities, but to minimize them. This is the paradox of imagination in science, that it has for its aim the impoverishment of imagination. By that outrageous phrase, I mean that the highest flight of scientific imagination is to weed out the proliferation of new ideas. In science, the grand view is a miserly view, and a rich model of the universe is one which is as poor as possible in hypotheses.

This is indeed the description, not only of the practice of science, but of its temperament. The Greeks peopled nature with a rowdy, happy-go-lucky train of gods and spirits. Science arrived like an Old Testament prophet, with a puritan and obsessed vision of single-minded coherence, to sweep that pagan plenty out of the window and put in its place the Jehovah who orders all things under laws. That is no less an imaginative vision than that of poetry: the Old Testament is as full of ecstasy as the New. But it is a different kind of ecstasy, an ascetic and implosive imagination which I shall contrast in my next essay with the prodigal explosive imagination of poetry.

Three

✠

KNOWLEDGE OF THE SELF

On 26 May 1777 Mr. J. Scott wrote to the Reverend Mr. Whisson of Trinity College, Cambridge a letter which was later published in the *Philosophical Transactions* of the Royal Society in London. I quote part of this letter.

I do not know any green in the world; a pink colour and a pale blue are alike, I do not know one from the other. A full red and a full green the same, I have often thought them a good match; but yellows (light, dark, and middle) and all degrees of blue, except those very pale, commonly called sky, I know perfectly well, and can discern a deficiency, in any of those colours, to a particular nicety: a full purple and deep blue sometimes baffle me. I married my daughter to a genteel, worthy man a few years ago; the day before the marriage he came to my house, dressed in a new suit of fine cloth cloaths. I was much displeased that he should come (as I supposed) in black: said, He should go back to change his colour. But my daughter said, No, no; the colour is very genteel; that it was my eyes that deceived me. He was a gentleman of the law, in a fine rich claret-coloured dress, which is as much a black to my eyes as any black that ever was dyed.

This is one of the first descriptions in human history of the fairly common failing of red-green color blindness. It was prompted by a report at second hand of a more extreme form of color blindness a few months earlier in 1777, and that is the first certain record that we have. Later in the century, in 1794, the great chemist John Dalton gave a detailed account of his own confusion of red and green, and for a time his defect (which was like

Mr. Scott's—he saw 'not much difference in colour between a stick of red sealing wax and grass') went by his name. So far as we know, no one had given thought to these striking failings, which crudely limit the spectrum of visual experience, before the eighteenth century.

This is surely a remarkable state of affairs. Some form of red-green color deficiency is perhaps the most common of male defects. Where it has been looked for, between six percent and eight percent of men are found to suffer from it—say, one man in every fifteen. What we know about its mode of inheritance, which is itself interesting, suggests that this percentage has been stable all through historical times. That is, one man in fifteen has been more or less insensitive to the difference between red and green all through the time that literature has been written about the beauty of nature, the dazzle of the rainbow and the sunset, and the brilliant hues of flowers and birds. The colors in ancient mosaics, the gorgeous dyes that the Mediterranean artificers extracted from unlikely plants and animals to give splendor to their ceremonial clothes, the precious stones in the breastplate of the high priest in Jerusalem—all these were chosen for, and sometimes chosen by, many men who (in Mr. Scott's vivid phrase) saw 'a full red and a full green the same, I have often thought them a good match'. Perhaps Homer called the sea *wine-dark* not to be colorful, but because he was color-blind. Less than two hundred years before Mr. Scott, Shakespeare made Macbeth say:

Will all great *Neptunes* Ocean wash this blood
Cleane from my Hand? no: this my Hand will rather
The multitudinous Seas incarnadine,
Making the Greene one, Red.

Yet one in fifteen of the men who heard this could not always tell green from red.

This ignorance was not part of any general neglect of science. Farfetched observations and delicate experiments had been made long before Mr. Scott's day, and thoughtful theories had been built on them. The great work in mechanics by Galileo, Johann Kepler and Isaac Newton was done and done with in the seventeenth century. William Gilbert had written his book on the magnet long ago, and had speculated about electricity; and Benjamin Franklin had even flown his kite in an electric storm before 1777.

Nor were their discoveries confined to natural science. Galileo had held his pulse and timed a pendulum by it almost two hundred years before. William Harvey had found the circulation of the blood. Indeed, the scientist of those centuries commonly began as a medical man, and observed and experimented on men before nature. Active and inquiring men have always turned their curiosity actively on themselves—and color blindness is literally a defect of men: it is rare among women.

Of course, color blindness could not have gone unremarked for thousands of years if it had troubled those who suffer from it as toothache and dropsy do. It does not: it is not a gross affliction that calls aloud for correction. The sense of color rounds out our experience in a more modest way. It spins a relation between us and the world which is not charged with the commands for action that other sensations urge on us. Naturally, we should not like to live in the world of the black and white photograph, but we could put up with it; after all, most animals do—and so, we feel sure, do machines.

Color belongs to the range of experiences which art and poetry explore. Late in the seventeenth century, Robert Hooke's scientific study of the iridescent colors on the wings of insects and birds, and Newton's wonderful analysis of the spectrum, impressed and influenced poets: they made them use more color words. But they did not cause poets and their readers to notice the oddities of visual experience, because that is not the way in which poetry engages our experience. Color blindness continued to go unobserved, not because poets are unobservant, but because the questions that they ask of experience are different in kind from those that scientists ask.

2

We might conclude from this that poets do not bother much with the realities of human experience. But we would be quite wrong. Turn back to the lines that I quoted from Shakespeare. They are from that muffled scene of terror when Macbeth has just murdered for the first time, and comes distraught to his wife with the bloody daggers in his hands. She takes them from him, and in the hush there is a sudden knocking at the gate. De Quincey has an essay on the dramatic power of the knocking, and it haunts Lady Macbeth's sleep later in the play. But here it is still Macbeth who flinches.

> Whence is that knocking?
> How is't with me, when euery noyse appalls me?
> What Hands are here? hah: they pluck out
>   mine Eyes.
> Will all great *Neptunes* Ocean wash this blood
> Cleane from my Hand? no: this my Hand
>   will rather
> The multitudinous Seas incarnardine,
> Making the Greene one, Red.

The sense of hysteria here is precise and powerful. It is the same everywhere in the play, a masterful and mounting horror that at last grows larger than Macbeth and his wife. Shakespeare understood their characters perfectly. They are, as it were, prisoners in the squirrel cage of machination which she has tripped; when they lose their nerve, it rolls over them.

The final irony comes near the end of the play, full

circle, when the beleaguered Macbeth hears another sudden noise.

> MACBETH. What is that noyse?
> SEYTON. It is the cry of women, my good Lord.
> MACBETH. I haue almost forgot the taste of Feares:
>   The time ha's beene, my sences would haue cool'd
>   To heare a Night-shrieke, and my Fell of haire
>   Would at a dismall Treatise rowze, and stirre
>   As life were in't. I haue supt full with horrors,
>   Direnesse familiar to my slaughterous thoughts
>   Cannot once start me. Wherefore was that cry?
> SEYTON. The Queene (my Lord) is dead.
> MACBETH. She should haue dy'de heereafter;
>   There would haue beene a time for such a word.

This is the saddest speech in the play: the gray epitaph to the wife who has set in train the lumbering machinery of disaster that in the end has crushed both bone and flesh—judgment and feeling.

Between the first noise and the last, husband and wife have changed places: slowly they have exchanged characters. There is a moment of crossing when Macbeth asks a question for them both.

> Can'st thou not Minister to a minde diseas'd,
> Plucke from the Memory a rooted Sorrow,
> Raze out the written troubles of the Braine,
> And with some sweet Obliuious Antidote
> Cleanse the stufft bosome, of that perillous stuffe
> Which weighes vpon the heart?

Is this a practical question? Yes—it is sensible and revealing, the kind of question that the patient's husband asks of the doctor, in a whisper, outside a thousand consulting rooms. Naturally, the doctor replies stiffly that he is not an analyst:

> Therein the Patient
> Must minister to himselfe.

Yet we know very well that this is not the burden of Macbeth's question, and that the answer is not a pedantic medical No. Macbeth is asking an unanswerable question, not about his wife but about himself, and not of the doctor but of himself. How has he come to be where he is? Was this written in his character as an inexorable fate? What conspiracy lured him from one deceiving, self-deceiving step to another? Macbeth knows as plainly as his wife in her sleep that no step can be undone, that every step has been fatal, and that there is not now and never has been any other way to go. This is the burden of Macbeth's question, and it is breaking him. His answer to the doctor's prim professional wisdom is bleak and perfunctory, obstinate yet hopeless.

> Throw Physicke to the Dogs, Ile none of it.
> Come, put mine Armour on.

We might be tempted to conclude that this is fantastic, had we not ourselves watched Hitler walk this way to destruction, unswerving as a somnambulist, and burn Berlin over his head.

So we must conclude something else: that the colored imagery of poetry is a good form for uncovering and carrying the sensations of fear, ambition, hysteria and despair, and yet an inefficient form for discovering and communicating the sensations of color. I will quote another speech by Macbeth in which the imagery of color is universal.

> Come, seeling Night,
> Skarfe vp the tender Eye of pittifull Day,
> And with thy bloodie and inuisible Hand
> Cancell and teare to pieces that great Bond,
> Which keepes me pale. Light thickens,
> And the Crow makes Wing toth' Rookie Wood:
> Good things of Day begin to droope, and drowse,
> Whiles Nights black Agents to their Prey's doe rowse.

The gory hands and the colors of fear: these Macbeth has right to the last detail. Here Shakespeare was at one with his heroes, and knew that what went on in his head also went on in theirs. What he did not know was that inside these same heads, one in fifteen physically could not fully picture what the sea looks like when it fills with blood.

3

The mode of knowledge that I have begun to trace in *Macbeth* is characteristic of literature, and I shall examine it in this essay. I think that the same mode of knowledge, which I call knowledge of the self, underlies all the arts. Nevertheless, I shall keep my examples to literature, and for the most part to poetry. My reason is practical: literature lends itself to discussion, and displays its meanings, more transparently than, say, painting and music do. Certainly I can speak about what literature says to me more clearly than I can about any other art.

In particular, literature is written in much the same language as science, and the comparison between them is therefore direct and critical. I believe that whatever is found in this comparison to characterize literature also characterizes the other arts. But it does not matter if I am wrong, and if literature is more special than I suppose. My purpose in this essay is to present a kind of knowledge which is as imaginative as science, and yet which is a different kind: not only knowledge of something else, but in a different mode. It will suffice for my purpose if I find another mode in one art: say, in poetry.

Let me then look at a whole, compact poem. It is by Robert Frost. He is not as high-pitched as Shakespeare; the poem has no bright and wistful imagery of evocation; but neither is it one of those milk and honey, milk and

water poems into which Frost often lapsed. It is a tough
and searching and extraordinary poem, and it is called,
Provide, Provide.

> The witch that came (the withered hag)
> To wash the steps with pail and rag,
> Was once the beauty Abishag,
>
> The picture pride of Hollywood.
> Too many fall from great and good
> For you to doubt the likelihood.
>
> Die early and avoid the fate.
> Or if predestined to die late,
> Make up your mind to die in state.
>
> Make the whole stock exchange your own!
> If need be occupy a throne,
> Where nobody can call *you* crone.
>
> Some have relied on what they knew;
> Others on being simply true.
> What worked for them might work for you.
>
> No memory of having starred
> Atones for later disregard,
> Or keeps the end from being hard.
>
> Better to go down dignified
> With boughten friendship at your side
> Than none at all. Provide, provide!

The imagery of this poem belongs to our own age. It
uses the verb *to star*, for example, not for poetic effect,
but simply to describe what a Hollywood celebrity does.
Elsewhere it chooses equally direct phrases of today,
such as the command to make the whole stock exchange
your own. That is, the poem is deliberately worded to
draw in fields of experience which we will feel to bear
on and to have a part in our own lives.

The story in the poem is also clear and contemporary. The poet meets a woman who has been a star in her past, and now she is nothing. Such stories needed and need no inventing. As I write this essay, the death is announced in Nice of Caroline Otero, the last of the famous cocottes of the nineties. Toulouse-Lautrec put her on a poster which is still printed, and Paris feasted and adored and paid her, and in time forgot her. She lived to be ninety-six, poor as a mouse, with nothing left at the last but (it was rumored) a hoarded bundle of worthless Czarist bonds. If that rumor is true, it gives her story an irony still tarter than Frost's.

Frost drily reflects that people have feared and faced their decline in old age in several ways. We can avoid it by dying early; but if we must grow old, then we had better ensure that we keep our dignity at any price—even if we have to buy it. The moral would be (if there were a moral), Do not become a fallen star: provide for your survival, whatever its cost, by any means at all, however mercenary, trivial, or tawdry.

But do we really think there is a moral? Do we know whose side we are on, or Robert Frost is? And do we truly believe that Frost means to lay down a rule that it is better to provide for old age by buying friends, than to live with the memory of having starred? Of course not; the poet is not giving this advice—and neither is he giving the opposite advice. The climax of the poem is not the cynical, truculent handshake of the last verse, the message to the middle-aged man going west:

> Better to go down dignified
> With boughten friendship at your side
> Than none at all. Provide, provide!

The climax has come in the two verses before that, which soberly set out the human dilemma with no pretense that it can be resolved by any moralizing rule.

Some have relied on what they knew;
Others on being simply true.
What worked for them might work for you.

No memory of having starred
Atones for later disregard,
Or keeps the end from being hard.

The poet is not giving advice at all. He is not asking us to accept a moral, or even to draw one for ourselves. The universe of art is one in which there is a suspension of decisions, what Samuel Taylor Coleridge called a willing suspension of disbelief: a suspension of the sense of judgment.

There are no morals in a poem; there are no morals in any work of art. There are no specific lessons to be learned and there is no advice to be followed. There are many implications in a poem which enrich our experience of life: but it is a many-sided experience, and we are not asked to come down on one side or another. Robert Frost with a macabre sense of humor, pretending to teach a lesson which he does not want us to learn, epitomizes the nature of art. Here the imagination explores the alternatives of human action without ever deciding for one rather than another. And in this tense and happy indecision, and only in this, the work of art is different from the work of science.

4

This is the cardinal point about the experience that the work of art provides. We do not at the end of it have a recipe for action. *Macbeth* and Robert Frost do not teach us to forswear ambition, and neither do they teach us to pursue it. The poem provides an experience at the end of which we do not hold that one line of action has been proved right and the other wrong. It is a provoked and simulated experience which we have gone out of our way to enter, by choice and for our own ends, and in that important sense it is an experiment. Exactly as in science, we have rearranged nature for our own experiment. But the purpose of the experiment is different in science and in art. The aim of the scientific experiment is to choose between alternative hypotheses, and to decide that one procedure is effective and another is not. A scientific experiment is intended to lead us to single-valued action. The experiment of poetry is not.

And in the logical sciences, this is even clearer. If logic asserts the proposition *P*, then it denies the proposition *not-P*. We are free in logic to say, if we believe it true, that love is simple, or blissful, or carnal; but we cannot then logically say of the same love that it is complex, or anguished, or spiritual. Even if we have a more sophisticated logic, in which there is a third alternative to *P* and *not-P*, that alternative asserts that they are both meaningless. But in poetry, to assert *P* and *not-P* together is not meaningless: it is not meaningless to say that love is ordinary and extraordinary at the same time. On the contrary, poetry claims that it contains the very meaning of the experience of living.

Moreover, if a poem (however solemn or delightful) asserts less than that, it becomes trifling. It is not serious; it trifles with us; its message is memorizable but not memorable. Consider as a gay example one of the broadside ballads that Thomas d'Urfey collected in *Wit and Mirth: or Pills to Purge Melancholy* in 1719. A knight meets a lady:

> Quoth he, shall you and I Lady,
> Among the Grass lye down a;
>   And I will have a special Care,
>   Of rumpling of your Gown a.

The lady's answer has an inviting sound.

> If you will go along with me,
> Unto my Father's Hall, Sir;
>> You shall enjoy my Maiden-head,
>> And my Estate and all, Sir.

But when they get to her father's hall, she shuts the gate in his face, pays him off graciously, and gives him a lucid piece of worldly advice.

> And if you meet a Lady fair,
> As you go thro' the next Town, Sir;
> You must not fear the Dew of the Grass,
> Nor the rumpling of her Gown, Sir:
> And if you meet a Lady Gay,
> As you go by the Hill, Sir;
> If you will not when you may,
> You shall not when you will, Sir.

As a hawker's ballad, this is winning. But as a poem, it is as shallow as the code of conduct which it recommends: they both lack the play and the tension of human life. It asserts *P*, and its irony (unlike Frost's) is cynical, for it adds the rider that those who believe *not-P* are fools.

5

By contrast, a profound poem is not an exercise in resolution, and does not teach us to opt for one kind of action rather than another. The knowledge that we get from it does not tell us how to act, but how to be. A poem tells us how to be human by identifying ourselves with others, and finding again their dilemmas in ourselves. What we learn from it is self-knowledge.

I do not mean by this a narrow knowledge of our own foibles only. On the contrary, the self that we discover in this mode of knowledge is every self and is universal —the human self. Or better, each of us discovers the outline of his self within the human totality. We learn to recognize ourselves in others, and the character of others in ourselves. We compare ourselves with others, and the comparison shows us what we are and at the same time what man is, in general and in particular.

This analysis has a bearing on an odd puzzle in the theory of knowledge. It is easy for you and me to exchange knowledge about nature, because we both observe her from similar places: you from where you stand and I from where I stand. But can we exchange knowledge about the mind of one of us? I observe my mind from the inside, and you observe it from the outside; I am conscious of my thoughts and feelings in myself, but you infer them from my behavior. A. J. Ayer states the difficulty thus at the end of *The Problem of Knowledge:*

> If someone asks me whether I am in pain and I answer that I am, my reply, as I understand it, is not an answer to his question. For I am reporting the occurrence of a certain feeling; whereas, so far as he was concerned, his question could only have been a question about my physical condition. So also, if he says that my reply is false, he is not strictly contradicting me: for all that he can be denying is that I exhibited the proper signs of pain, and this is not what I asserted; it is what he understood me to be asserting but not what I understood myself.

The assumption here is that you must study my mind as you would study that of a Martian—or rather, as you would study a machine made by a Martian. I do not accept this assumption. On the contrary, I hold that there is good evidence in the structure of my brain and the behavior of my body that my mind (my whole mind, in Gilbert Ryle's sense) is cousin to yours. And if it is cousin to yours, if it is so far like yours, it probably works like yours: that is the more reasonable assumption from which to proceed until it is disproved. And this is much the reply that Ayer too makes to the difficulty.

What I am saying in this essay goes on from this: it turns the resolution of the difficulty into a policy. If my mind works like yours, then you can do more than believe what I say I feel: you can learn from it. By identifying yourself with me, you can learn new things about the human self, and about yourself not as one person but as one example. You enter more fully into your own mind by entering through me into the human mind. You will not get this knowledge from my sage philosophical advice, of course: that will only tell you how to act and to reason. But you will get it from my poetry—if it is good.

6

I am asserting that a poem informs us in a mode of knowledge that is many-valued, and that a scientific paper instructs us in a mode of knowledge that is single-valued. This says something quite different from the traditional assertion (which Aldous Huxley revived) that the language of poetry is ambiguous and personal and intense, and the language of science is exact and impersonal and general. Indeed (I repeat) it is not true that science, as a language of thought, is free from ambiguity. It could not be imaginative if it were; it would be closed and dead. In all living languages, the human mind plays with and explores the ambiguities that lie hidden in every general idea—that is, in every word. The difference lies elsewhere, in the different endeavors of science and literature. The scientific experiment is planned to be critical, so that we may have grounds for preferring one action to another. The experiment of literature parades its alternatives so that we may steep ourselves in them, and learn to know ourselves and others together.

The difference in endeavor between science and literature is nevertheless reflected in different uses of language. Science at any moment has a provisional language for the exposition of what is then known, as if it were final. Literature has no such language, for it cannot be rendered, even provisionally, as an exposition. Here the thought is still one with the language that expresses it: it forms and informs the sentence (and us) together.

For example, in the exposition of science there are no jokes, no irony, and (in particular) no puns. This may seem an odd thing to remark, yet it is characteristic. For the thought in the pun cannot be prised away from the words; it says nothing except exactly what it says. I quote one of the historic puns, ascribed in *Joe Miller's Jests or the Wit's Vade-Mecum* of 1739 to the famous Daniel Purcel.

> The same Gentleman as he had the Character of a great Punster, was desired one Night in Company, by a Gentleman, to make a *Pun extempore,* upon what Subject, said *Daniel,* the *King,* answered the other, the *King,* Sir, said he, is no *Subject.*

This is funny but seems trivial; yet it mirrors the play of wit, the tension of irony, in all literature. The king was a good subject just because he was no subject. The drama and the clowning of *King Lear* are shot through with this double meaning, of the king who gave away two halves of his kingdom and made himself a subject—a subject for scorn.

> LEAR. A bitter Foole.
> FOOLE. Do'st thou know the difference my Boy, betweene a bitter Foole, and a sweet one.
> LEAR. No Lad, teach me.
> FOOLE. Nunckle, giue me an egge, and Ile giue thee two Crownes.
> LEAR. What two Crownes shall they be?

FOOLE. Why after I haue cut the egge i'th'middle
and eate vp the meate, the two Crownes of the
egge.

This is no longer funny, because it is too bitter. But it has
the wry essence of humor, which lies in the play of two
opposing meanings, neither of which is intended to oust
the other—even when, as here (or in a Shaggy Dog
story), they are incompatible. It is as if we were putting
together two pieces of folk wisdom, such as 'Two heads
are better than one', yet 'Too many cooks spoil the broth';
or 'Look before you leap', yet 'He who hesitates is lost'.
We are not meant to take an instruction from either—
and neither from Lear nor his 'bitter Foole'.

7

King Lear contains two characters who contrast two
views of the world that are familiar in philosophy as well
as in literature. They are the two sons of Gloucester:
Edmund, the natural or bastard son, and the true-born
Edgar who, in the order of nature, ought to succeed.
Their relation, and the undertone of the play, is a constantly restless pun which at once confounds and confronts the two opposed meanings of nature. Edmund
speaks for Epicurean nature, the chaotic play of atoms
in which there is no law but the survival of the fittest.

Thou Nature are my Goddesse, to thy Law
My seruices are bound,

are his first words.

Why brand they vs
With Base? With basenes Barstadie? Base, Base?
Who in the lustie stealth of Nature, take
More composition, and fierce qualitie,
Then doth within a dull stale tyred bed

Goe to th'creating a whole tribe of Fops
Got'tweene a sleepe, and wake?

Naturally, this bastard's nature (sinister as his conception) flies plumb in the face of the grave Stoic dispensation in which everything has a natural place—a place
ordained by its nature and by all nature. So the unnatural
events unroll: Lear gives up his place to his daughters,
Edgar is tricked and forced to fly from his, Edmund
climbs higher (into the beds of the greedy daughters),
and Gloucester is brutally blinded.

The yonger rises, when the old doth fall.

In the orgy of ingratitude between fathers and children,
children and fathers, Lear has gone mad, and cried into
the storm,

Thou all-shaking Thunder,
Strike flat the thicke Rotundity o'th'world,
Cracke Natures moulds, all germaines spill at once
That makes ingratefull Man.

Shakespeare took the two views of nature, Epicurean
and Stoic, from talk that was in the air at the time. The
concept of nature was much bandied and debated then.
Even the phrase *natural son* flatly changed its meaning
during Shakespeare's life—it meant a son born in wedlock
when he was born, and a bastard before he died. The
Renaissance nature was at odds with the tradition of
order and degree in his mind. Whiffs of Italian science
were blowing into England by the time that he was writing *King Lear* in 1606. It is not likely that Shakespeare
had yet heard of Galileo. But he surely had heard of
Giordano Bruno, who had caused a scandal at Oxford
when he lectured on the new science of Copernicus in
1583, and a hush in Europe when the Inquisition burned
him in 1600.

And the two conceptions of nature, the small-scale disorder and the large-scale order, the statistical play be-

tween them—these are the very stuff of modern science.
But in science, they have to be resolved: the debate between waves and particles in quantum physics is exactly
a part of this resolution. We do not know whether nature
is made of waves or particles. The fact is, we do not
know what basic stuff she is made of—and if we knew,
we could not understand it otherwise than by analogy.
But we act in science with decision in the face of these
uncertainties. We form theories which resolve, locally
and for specific uses, the conflict between the two concepts.

The point of *King Lear* and of all literature, tragic or
comic, is that there is no such resolution. *King Lear* is not
a blueprint nor a primer of geometry. It does not imply,
say (as the brilliant thought of Galois did), that it is im-
possible to trisect an angle. It does not even imply that it
is impolitic to trisect a kingdom. The plot was not chosen
to warn us against that headstrong gesture of Lear's, even
by the way. Instead, we learn to immerse ourselves in
the human situation. We become one with the characters
in the play because they are alive and are like us and like
all men and women. We get inside them, and thereby
understand better how to live inside ourselves; we stretch
the skin of isolation inside which each of us lives. But it
is by no means evident that we know how to act better
in any specific encounter.

8

The unresolved choice between two directions of action,
the human predicament, is hidden in every work of literature. It is present even when a character seems to be
shown as all bad. Edmund in *King Lear* engages our
sympathy (just that: he entangles it) even when we
would rather have his brother Edgar for company. When
Lady Macbeth walks in her sleep, we do not smugly

say that she should have known she was driving herself
to a nervous breakdown. We do not think of her crimes
but of her; we see that she has become their victim and
her own; we think of ourselves in her, and we say what
her doctor says,

> God, God forgiue vs all.

Since I have quoted a poem by Robert Frost, let me
make the point by quoting a harsh poem about Frost by
a younger poet, John Berryman: one of three written, in
his phrase, 'around the Old Gentleman'.

> His malice was a pimple down his good
> big face, with its sly eyes. I must be sorry
> Mr Frost has left:
> I like it so less I don't understood—
> he couldn't hear or see well—all we sift—
> but this is a *bad* story.
>
> He had fine stories and was another man
> in private; difficult, always. Courteous,
> on the whole, in private.
> He apologize to Henry, off & on,
> for two blue slanders; which was good of him.
> I don't know how he made it.
>
> Quickly, off stage with all but kindness, now.
> I can't say what I have in mind. Bless Frost,
> any odd god around.
> Gentle his shift, I decussate & command,
> stoic deity. For a while here we possessed
> an unusual man.

We might suppose that this embarrassing portrait could
wake no echo of sympathy in any one of us. The faults
that are imputed to Frost are not even heroic: they are
petty. Yet we should be wrong. On the contrary, the
portrait is human, and makes us aware that we too suffer
from the same shortcomings, and have yielded to the

same temptations. These vices, these very vices, are as much a part of our humanity as of Robert Frost's. The poet's tone in the end is less cruel than ironic in teasing Frost with being neither monster nor superman, but 'an unusual man' with the usual character.

But we must not stop with Lady Macbeth and Robert Frost. Our sympathies are not yet drained when we have pitied her and been tolerant to him. Literature taps still deeper and more secret springs of feeling and understanding. In the end, the undeviating disaster of Macbeth, who admits no breaking point, shakes us with a more violent compassion than his broken wife. And we can feel the same compassion and the same horrifying recognition of our selves in characters whom their authors plainly detested. John Dryden was in a deadly rage when he drew the famous portrait of the first Earl of Shaftesbury in *Absalom and Achitophel* in 1681.

Of these the false *Achitophel* was first,
A Name to all succeeding Ages curst.
For close Designs and crooked Counsels fit,
Sagacious, Bold, and Turbulent of wit,
Restless, unfixt in Principles and Place,
In Pow'r unpleased, impatient of Disgrace;
A fiery Soul, which working out its way, ⎫
Fretted the Pigmy Body to decay: ⎬
And o'r informed the Tenement of Clay. ⎭
A daring Pilot in extremity;
Pleas'd with the Danger, when the Waves went high
He sought the Storms; but, for the Calm unfit,
Would Steer too nigh the Sands to boast his Wit.
Great Wits are sure to Madness near alli'd
And thin Partitions do their Bounds divide;
Else, why should he, with Wealth and Honour blest,
Refuse his Age the needful hours of Rest?
Punish a Body which he coud not please,
Bankrupt of Life, yet Prodigal of Ease?

And all to leave what with his Toil he won
To that unfeather'd two-legg'd thing, a Son.

We feel in such a passage a tug of war between the
writer's scorn and his grudging admiration, and we end
by discounting the scorn because it is personal: Dryden
hated the man. But what he hated in the man is not in
the portrait and, at bottom, is not in the character as
we are made to see it. The vices of the character dwarf
the pigmy body and make a monster; and in the monster
we recognize, gigantic, our own traits.

This point is cardinal. The most moving experience of
literature makes us aware that we too are swept by the
waves of lust and destruction that overwhelm other men.
We too taste in inner agony the salt tang of cruelty that
we call inhuman, and learn that it is most human. We
have it in us to be murderers and con-men and perverts
and the scum of the earth. Charles Dickens when he
read in public wanted always to play Bill Sikes and to
murder Nancy. And Cordelia in *King Lear*, although she
is the heroine, is as crippled by her alienation from feeling as any modern delinquent in the novels of Alberto
Moravia. Creon in Sophocles and Jean Anouilh is us;
Caligula in history and in Camus is us—is, but for the
grace of God, us. Literature is not a suburban gallery of
worthies. On the contrary, it is more often a picaresque
ragbag of rogues and fallen women, of Doctor Faustus
and Madame Bovary, of Falstaff and Mrs. Bloom, because our identity with them needs most to be evoked, in
passion and compassion. Othello and Iago and Desde-
mona, all three, are tragic figures because they are so full
of faults, and the faults are ours.

The sense of community with others that makes the
experience of poetry cannot be formalized; we are not
anywhere in sight of putting it on a tape. It cannot even
be animalized, if I can use that obsolete word to recall
that Descartes held that animals are automata. For an-

imals lack both kinds of imagination. They plainly lack the scientific imagination to invent, say, the electric current. But they also lack the poetic imagination, the ability to enter the feelings of others from the inside, that shudders yet delights to give an electric shock—in fun or in the torture chamber. Animals do not devise the concentration camps, because they are not clever enough, of course. But neither do they staff them; it is not true that the camps were run by beasts—they were run by men; the pleasure is as peculiar to man as the invention. Animals are not murderers, are not cruel, are not driven by the wretchedness of the Marquis de Sade and Jean Genet. This is the bitter thought that made Jonathan Swift, who passionately wanted only to be reasonable, prefer the Houyhnhnms to the Yahoos.

9

Other philosophers before me have remarked that a man understands other men more directly than he understands nature. Early in this century, they invented the word *empathy*, and though that has since turned out to be too general, it has my sense. About the same time, Max Weber used the German verb *verstehen* for the way in which we understand the motives of others. Yet his meaning (and Dilthey's before him and Jaspers's since) is not mine, because it still treats that mode of understanding as a scientific mode: it seeks rules to unravel the courses of social and personal history as we seek to unravel the course of nature.

For the same reason, I am not content to stop at the analysis of Friedrich Hayek, and of Michael Polanyi after him, which shows that human beings understand and obey many rules which they cannot write out fully. For this analysis, admirable as it is, is as apt to science as to conduct, and therefore says only what I said in my second essay: that all our descriptions of all nature carry a penumbra of uncertainty. In trying to formalize a rule, we look for truth, but what we find is knowledge, and what we fail to find is certainty. This limitation has no special bearing on the knowledge of self.

My meaning is different. I hold that each man has a self, and enlarges his self by his experiences. That is, he learns from experience: from the experiences of others as well as his own, and from their inner experiences as well as their outer. But he can learn from their inner experience only by entering it, and that is not done merely by reading a written record of it. We must have the gift to identify ourselves with other men, to relive their experience and to feel its conflicts as our own. And the conflicts are the essence of the experience. We gain knowledge of our selves by identifying ourselves with others, but that is not enough—that only gives us the fantasies of sex and the parodies of power, the absurd strutting daydreams of Secret Agent 007 and *Butterfield 8*. We must enter others in order to share their conflicts, and they must be shown to have grave conflicts, in order that we shall feel in their lives what we know in our own: the human dilemma. The knowledge of self cannot be formalized because it cannot be closed, even provisionally; it is perpetually open, because the dilemma is perpetually unresolved.

That is why poetry is full of questions, and they are not so much rhetorical as unanswerable. Whether the poet asks,

> O what can ail thee, knight-at-arms,

or

> Who is Silvia? What is she?

—whether he asks,

O wha will shoe my bonny foot?

or

Can'st thou not Minister to a minde diseas'd,

the reach of the question, when we follow it, turns out
to be bottomless. The questions in poetry are not asked
about specific actions and cannot be settled by specific
advice. The knowledge of self that we learn from them
is to ask the question at all—most often it would not have
occurred to us. It is not the form of the question that is
a surprise, but its being a question. And that cannot be
dealt with by any formal answer. When William Words-
worth asked,

O Cuckoo! shall I call thee Bird,
Or but a wandering Voice?

his self-searchings were not very profound, and they de-
served the irony of the wit who mocked,

State the alternative preferred,
With reasons for your choice.

But what A. E. Housman's irony implies (he is said to
have been the wit) is precisely that the questions of
poetry cannot be answered in the formula of the exami-
nation room.

10

The literature in which what I am saying is made most
visible is the drama, and that is why I have drawn on it
so often in this essay. It was not chance that made men
act out their lost and doomed adventures in ancient
Greece, and makes us still feel in them as if we were
drowning. The drama openly invites us to enter the lives
of other men, to become one not with one character but

with all, and to feel in our single self the conflicts that divide and entangle them. We play even as children and, unlike animals, we play at being other people. Animals are too direct for that; in play and in earnest, they act no part but themselves. They do not consciously mimic another animal of the species and they cannot imagine how it feels to be inside him.

This is the human character which the rituals of animals lack. Animals do behave in impractical and ceremonial ways. The great crested grebe invites the co-operation of his mate by presenting her (and she him) with pieces of weed. The fiddler crab goes through a pantomime of clashing his ornamental claw against his rival's, and hides for days if he feels himself defeated. Whatever practical aim these gestures once had has long gone, and their effect now is symbolic—they give, as it were, a psychological coherence to a group of animals, and thereby turn the group into a society. Yet there is nothing in these ritual acts which makes them like the Greek theater. Fantastic and enchanting as they are, they remain a formal means of communication. They signal the intention of one animal to another, and they invite agreement but not identification.

The drama as human ritual breaks out of this limitation. An actor is a man who must put himself into the skin of another man, even if, as in the Elizabethan theater, the other man is a young woman. And it is not enough for him to ape and physically to move into the gestures of the other man. That mechanical skill we can build into a machine, and indeed young animals have it in their play. A kitten pawing a ball of wool, a cub wrestling with another, experiment with gestures which they do not yet command, and by these trials reach into their future skill: they are, as it were, stretching into the adult. The movements of a child actor have some of the same awkward charm, the kittenish urge to become a cat and the comic sense of just falling short. But this is only half of what the child at play does. The other half is to think and feel himself into the man, and if he fails to convince, that is where he fails.

A young actress acts all the gestures of an old woman, and yet she fails to act an old woman, because she cannot think herself into that experience. She does not know what it is like to turn fewer heads, and then one, and then none. By contrast, Sarah Bernhardt in old age went on playing a girl in love, and is said to have played her very movingly. Perhaps she played her more movingly than a girl could, with a pathos which was not true to the part, and yet which was true for those who saw her—because, like her, they had once had greater hopes from love than had been fulfilled.

Machines do not act in plays, and animals do not pretend to be other animals; they do not know how. This is what cannot be mechanized, even in principle, by any procedure that we can yet foresee: that we can identify ourselves with the inner environment of others. We know what another man feels when he feels angry, because we have been angry ourselves. We know what tenderness feels like, and fear, and curiosity, and cruelty, and fun. Shakespeare knew how a wife feels hysteria, although he did not know how a man sees colors. Charles Darwin knew what his wife would feel if he embarrassed her. To be at ease is not a faculty like vision, and embarrassment is not a defect like color blindness; it is more like hysteria. When I said in my first essay that my flourish embarrassed my wife, I was conjuring up in us all her conflict of feelings; and we understood her because we have all shared all her conflicting feelings.

This mode of knowledge cannot be formalized; we cannot make a tape of the experience which will also carry our sense that we know what it is like. An account of an observation in science—say, of a transit of Venus—is intended to take the place of the experience; within some agreed tolerance, the account—the tape—is the experience, for the writer as well as for the reader. I do not mean, of course, the experience of discovery; that creative moment cannot be formalized, in any language; I mean the experience of observing nature. But we cannot observe men and give an account of that as we observe nature. The poem and the drama is not the experience except as we identify ourselves with it, and know what it feels like to have it. What distinguishes literature is that it cannot be understood unless we understand what it is like to be human.

11

I should be doing violence to my thought if I ended this essay in the triumphant tone of a biologist who has discovered the difference between men and women. Men and women are different, but they are vastly more alike than they are different. So science and literature are different, but they are vastly more alike than they are different. For what makes them different is their expression in action, but what makes them alike is their origin in imagination. And that origin is not common by accident: science and literature, science and art, belong together as matched halves of what is unique in human experience.

I have called the unique faculty in which they both begin the imagination, that is, the human faculty of operating in the mind with images of things which are not present to the senses. The largest hoard of images that we create, and the most powerful method that we have for using them, is language. For human language is not confined to communication, as that of animals is. The language of animals consists of signals—perhaps forty sounds and gestures to command action or attention (including attention to the emotions of the signaler). The human gift is to possess a second language in which a man converses with himself.

With this thinking language we debate and weigh, we search our minds, we find in our heads the likenesses that give life to our view of nature and of our selves. A large part of the new brain in man is set aside for storing and manipulating the concepts in this language. Wilder Penfield recounts the impatience of a man with an electrode in his brain who found that it inhibited him from saying the word *butterfly* when he was shown one. He snapped his fingers in frustration, and when the current was switched off he explained why: he had tried to say *moth* as a way out, and could not find that word either. The search within ourselves for such likenesses is the creative gift by which man commands the hidden potential in nature and in himself.

In my view, it is these imaginative processes which make up the general state that we call consciousness. In saying this, I am denying full consciousness to any other animal than man. That seems to me just, because no other animal seems to be able to draw a clear boundary between himself and his environment. His memory is too short and his habits are too strong to make him firmly distinguish what he does from what is happening to him. In this sense, there is a ground for saying that only man is fully conscious of himself.

Consciousness is not merely an awareness of self: it also demands that we should know where we stop and the environment begins. For this reason, consciousness is the spring in our understanding of nature as surely as of self. Indeed, we get the liveliest part of our self-knowledge by understanding the experiences of other people—and they are not us but our environment. It could be argued that if there were no other people, and a man's experience grew only from his meetings with stones and stars (I leave the cactus and the camel out of the reckoning), he might well remain a machine and have no consciousness. But this is a pointless fancy: our environment from childhood does include other people, and we fare poorly whenever it does not.

Nor is it enough to confine consciousness to the present. On the contrary, what makes animals impersonal is that they cannot reach back any distance into their past. They have only habit to do the work of memory. A man, to be conscious of what he is, must carry in his mind what he was; and therefore he must remember also what he was not—what his environment was. He must be able to recall what he no longer sees, and this is the crucial step that he takes as a baby, and that turns him (so to speak) from a puppy into a child. Some time at about six months old, he loses the limitation of the animal,

> Out of sight, out of mind,

and finds the formula for human memory,

> Absence makes the heart grow fonder.

It is memory that gives us the power of foresight: we push into the future with the images in which we fixed the past. Full consciousness therefore looks both ways, and its most important look (I think) is into the future. All biological processes are directed towards the future, but man is distinguished by being consciously directed— his consciousness includes the future.

This is not the usual view of consciousness, and yet it seems to me inescapable. Man is conscious that he is different from his environment. But more than this, he is conscious that he is alive; and this sense carries him from the past into the future. To be conscious is both to know and to imagine, and our humanity flows from this deep spring. When we imagine nature outside ourselves into the future, we create the mode of knowledge which is science. And when we imagine ourselves alive into the future, we create another mode: knowledge of the self. They are the inseparable halves of the identity of man.

Four

❦

THE MIND IN ACTION

I have been examining the identity of man through three essays, and it is timely to look back to see how far the analysis has come. Does a man, one man, have a personal identity which marks him off from any other man? And is this identity a special arrangement of mechanical parts, or is it a self which is more than the sum of its parts?

If man is endowed with gifts which cannot be mimicked by a machine, then they must be looked for outside his machinery. Inside the skin, there is no difference in principle between the software of the tissues and the hardware of more familiar engines. We shall not find a tenable distinction between a self and a machine within the body. If there is such a distinction, it must be contained in the total complex of the body and its environment together.

But neither must we assert that the unknown box of my self is a machine merely because it has wheels in it, or circuits of neurons and nerve fibers. What counts is the total context of the black box and its input and output. If we do not know how to write the input and the output formally on tapes of instruction, then we do not have a machine, however mechanical the intestines of the black box are inside my head. I do not argue here, and I have not argued in these essays, whether we might ultimately know how to mechanize the input of the brain to itself. My concern is to establish that the input which the brain prepares for itself from its own output, in one of its modes of knowledge, cannot be written as a formal tape of instruction for any machine that we understand, in principle. Until we find a concept of what a machine is which follows fundamentally different laws from any that we know now, my self contains a part that is certainly not a machine in any known sense.

My self in this sense is not a thing but a process, which at the end of my life will be made up of all the visible and invisible actions that I have carried out. At any moment, therefore, the changes in my self are expressed in the way in which I now carry out an action that I have carried out before. That way can only have been modified by the experiences that were sandwiched between the two actions. What lies between the actions is experience arranged toward future action—that is, knowledge.

One form of experience is got by observing the world. This scientific mode of knowledge is not (as used to be said) passive and neutral. Instead, we now know that our senses themselves interpret the world in the act of observing it. For example, the eye is arranged not to see points of light, but to read the shape of things into what it sees. The sense impressions do not come to the brain as blank signals, but as elaborately prearranged and biased messages. A message is built up in a to and fro between the outside world, the sense organs, the nervous system which carries and itself acts on the message, and the brain. All this gives a special character to the concepts that the brain forms. And since man alone among the animals forms general concepts, it gives a special character to his analysis of the world.

Not all experience is got by observing nature. There is a second mode of knowledge which differs from the procedures of science. In our relations with people, and even with animals, we understand their actions and motives because we have at some time shared them, so that we know them from the inside. We know what anger is, we learn an accent or the value of friendship, by directly entering into the experience. And by identifying ourselves with the experience of others, we enlarge our knowledge of ourselves as human beings: we gain self-knowledge.

2

Both science and literature are languages, some of whose words are particular names, but most of which necessarily stand for large classes or concepts. And it is not possible to have a language, it is certainly not possible to have a concept, without some ambiguity in it. In our own lifetime, we have seen that the most primitive scientific concepts, space, time, and mass, are as ambiguous, and contain meanings as unexpected, as the literary concept of carnal love. It is not here that the difference between science and the arts lies.

What distinguishes the language of science from that of literature is something else. It begins in our ability, our very sophisticated ability, to find concepts and relations in nature which do not ask us to identify ourselves with her processes. The gradual evolution of science makes this plain, for if anything it has been harder there than in poetry to get rid of the pathetic fallacy that nature behaves as men do. John Milton was no longer serious when he wrote, more than three hundred years ago,

> Thee Shepherd, thee the Woods, and desert Caves,
> With wilde Thyme and the gadding Vine o'regrown,
> And all their echoes mourn.
> The Willows, and the Hazle Copses green,
> Shall now no more be seen,
> Fanning their joyous Leaves to thy soft layes.

No poet believed these fancies by the time Milton wrote. Yet many men with a scientific bent were then still trying to project human behavior into nature by sympathetic magic; or to read nature as an omen of human destiny, in astrology. The vocabulary of science contains many concepts that record the human wish to personify nature, and to find our sensations in her—force, inertia, energy,

work, the idea of error or tolerance, and even the sense
of time. Indeed, I rate the elucidation by Albert Einstein
of the true place of the observer in the meaning of time
as an intellectual liberation, as profound in the history
of science as the discovery of number.

William Blake wrote, surprisingly,

> As the true method of knowledge is experiment,
> the true faculty of knowing must be the faculty
> which experiences. This faculty I treat of.

Reading a poem is an experiment, exactly as rigging up
Foucault's pendulum for yourself is. The one like the
other is a contrived experience which others have had
and which you now go out of your way to seek. Neither of
them leads to a unique conclusion. The difference between them is this. In the experiment with the pendulum,
you resolve the ambiguity in the conclusions (for the
turn of its plane, like any scientific result, could be explained by many different laws) by opting for one of
them. In the experiment of literature, you do not resolve
the ambiguities; you remain aware that all the attitudes
to life which the work implies are tenable, and all are
your own.

We get rid of ambiguity in science by decision. We
make provisional assertions that the world is organized
in such a way, and not a more complex way; and we give
to these inductions a status which we cannot justify, but
which justifies itself by its success—so long as the success
continues. By contrast, literature does not try to provoke
in us the response of action, and therefore does not need
to resolve its ambiguities. We feel ourselves within all the
actors in the drama, and we are not asked to judge their
behavior by its effectiveness. We are not asked to judge
their behavior at all.

It follows that we derive different modes of knowledge from science and from literature. In science, knowledge is fixed in the single conclusion, which we accept

(for the time being) as definite. That can be put on a
tape, and can be used (so long as we maintain that conclusion) as a mechanical input to the machinery of the
brain. Science begins in our consciousness that our environment is not us. But the experiment of literature
opens another mode of knowledge, which we do not
know how to feed into any machine whose principle of
operation we can now conceive. We learn from it an
enlargement and a sharpening of our sympathy; we enter
the contraries of the human predicament more fully. We
know better what it feels like to be cowed, perverse, in
love, to be embarrassed and to blush for someone else.
And this begins in our consciousness that we are alive.
There is nothing supernatural about this. It simply says
that we know what it is like for a man to be tired, and
for a dog—dog-tired; but we do not know what it is like
for a metal to be fatigued.

3

I must now move away from the experimental conditions
of the scientific paper and the work of art to the daily
reality of human culture. And I use that word designedly,
because it has two senses, and I am about to change from
one to the other. Having discussed the deep but narrow
cultures of literature and science, I now turn to the broad
culture of social life.

A culture is something that each of its members learns.
It must be capable of being learned by the young, and of
being taught by the old. Of course, there are idiots and
delinquents in any culture who fail to learn, either for
physical or for psychological reasons. For the rest, they
can and do learn. For example, it seems certain that the
children of any tribe in the world, white, yellow, brown,
or black, can learn to make the sounds of any human
language. These include the complicated clicks of the

Bantu languages which, it turns out, Bantu children find just as difficult as we do. The Bantus leave out the clicks when they tell stories to their children, and when they make the animals in their own tales speak in baby talk.

There are several different ways of learning. In a culture, imitation is the most usual way, as Gabriel Tarde showed long ago. Yet we need to define imitation more narrowly than he did, and to use it more strictly. Margaret Mead gives the modern view of this and other ways of learning in a passage in *Continuities in Cultural Evolution* which I will quote in full.

In every human society and among many nonhuman creatures, the young learn from the adults and the newcomers to the group learn from the older members in a way which is conveyed by a rather loose use of the word *empathy,* or *Einfühlung,* a German psychological term which was originally used to describe an overall response to the form of a situation, as when an individual experienced discomfort if a picture hung askew on the wall. Empathy is a far simpler and more global concept than either imitation or identification, both of which are involved in much inexplicit, nonverbal, nonformalized learning.

The difference may be illustrated by a consideration of the Manus children's responses, in 1928. When I showed these children a pencil with a human, rather protuberant bust—which I had taken along just as a miscellaneous item that might amuse them—they immediately threw out their own chests in the posture of the bust. They could not be said to be *imitating* the pencil head as a whole, nor could they be said to be *identifying* with it. Rather, they were acting out the feeling of having one's chest stick out, which was conveyed to them visually by the humorous little pencil top.

But when a Manus child learns from an adult or

older child how to say a word, for example the phrase for "I don't want to," *pa pwen*, the teacher sets up an imitative singsong: the child says *pa pwen*, the adult says *pa pwen*, the child says *pa pwen*, and this may go on, especially if the teacher is only slightly older or rather dull mentally, as many as sixty times. Here the learning can be said to proceed by *imitation* of a specific act—in this case a verbal utterance. The teaching elder is imitated by the child, and the imitation is facilitated by the elder then imitating the child's performance.

But social behavior also runs much deeper than these mechanically learned imitations. One root of social life is our confidence that we understand what other people want, with all its inconsistencies, because we want it too. Public opinion polls and statistics sustain or shake that confidence but do not take its place. And again, there is nothing recondite about our understanding: it is grounded in social and physical experience. By way of example, I will begin with the physical experience of the kinesthetic sense.

4

The classical count of the five senses fell short by several; and among those it overlooked is the sense of kinesthesis. Since the word was only coined in 1880, knowledge of this sixth sense is fairly modern. I quote the dictionary definition:

> The sense of muscular effort that accompanies a voluntary motion of the body.

Thus the kinesthetic sense is an inner signal that runs parallel with our own outward action. It is easy to guess at an evolutionary reason for that—which means, as usual,

a reason written in teleological form, as if it had been de-
signed by a maker for a purpose. For we surely need a
sense of effort as we need the sensation of pain, to warn
us when we are approaching the limits of what the body
can sustain.

Both the kinesthetic sense and the sensation of pain
are also paths by which we enter the actions of other living things. Pain fires in us a kinship with other creatures
which, in its extreme form, expresses itself in sadism, in
masochism, and in the literature of terror, even when it is
as respectable as Edgar Allan Poe. The sense of kinesthesis is broader and more homely, and constantly and
cheerfully makes us share the everyday behavior of
others. We know in watching what it feels like to lift a
heavy weight, to balance precariously, to make a beautiful stroke at tennis, to skate and to dance. This is the
sense that prompts the passenger in a car to put his foot
hard on an imaginary brake whenever he fervently hopes
that the driver will.

Lest you should think that this is a civilized foible, turn
to the filmed pictures that Wolfgang Köhler took of his
young chimpanzees. Some of them, and chiefly Sultan,
were much better than others at the tasks of balancing
and building which Köhler set them. But the remarkable
pictures in Köhler's collection are not those of Sultan doing the tricks. Instead, they are pictures of Sultan and
other chimpanzees standing by, watching with an ago-
nized sense of participation while one of their clumsier
fellows tries a trick laboriously. As patently as the passenger in an errant car, the watcher cramps his body in a
kinesthetic gesture that acts out in imagination the action that he feels more vividly than he sees it.

You may think that Sultan's gestures, and ours that we
recognize in him, are merely passes of sympathetic magic,
and that they are made in the hope of influencing the
awkward chimpanzee or driver. After all, bowlers in
America and England at their different games make ab-

surd flutters after the ball has left their hands, as if to conjure it to go where they have failed to send it. But this explanation is back to front. Chimpanzees make no gestures to influence nature; and we must conclude that the bowler's pantomime derives from the kinesthetic sense, and not the other way about.

The kinesthetic gestures stretch naturally into the forms of ritual. Before they go out to hunt dangerous animals, many tribes have a ceremony of incantation, and it commonly includes some hunting actions. These actions have been described so often that we accept their presence as self-evident. Yet what can be their purpose? They are said to give the hunters courage. But it would be truer to say that they give them the feel of the hunt: they make the Pygmy hunters at home with the pursuit, and take them into its coming turns and surprises with the sense of action already in their muscles.

I think that this also is the magical meaning of the paintings of wild bulls and boars in the caves of Lascaux and elsewhere. They are (I think) a visual pantomime, by which the hunter immerses himself in the hunt and feels himself into its crises in advance. The instant when the bull turns is fixed for him, and flexes his spear arm (there are spears in the paintings) each time he sees it. The painter has frozen the moment of fear, and the hunter enters it through the painting as if through an air-lock.

5

I have been describing, by way of example, one means by which a culture binds its members together in a common identity. My example was the physical sense of kinesthesis, which causes us to feel our own gestures—and to feel also the echo, as it were, of the gestures of others. This community of action is evident in many ritual and ceremonial customs. We see it, for example, in the group dances of primitive tribes. For those who take part in these dances are not taught their parts as if they were children learning to speak. They learn from one another in unison by the kinesthetic sense. And the watchers feel at one with the dancers because they also feel themselves into the dance: they are (literally) swayed by the single action of the crowd.

It is a step—a crucial step—from acting a gesture to acting a person. I made this point in my third essay, and it is as true of daily life as of the drama. We come to play the part in society to which we aspire by proudly learning to act it. Thus Margaret Mead goes on, in the passage from which I have been quoting, to describe how a child learns his place in the culture of a Pacific island.

> Among the Manus one can also recognize *identification* behavior in the way in which a little boy reproduces the exact stance, walk, and tone of voice of his father. So, in 1928, it was possible to estimate the entrepreneurial status of the father by the posture and tone of his six-year-old, own or adopted son. It is necessary to invoke the concept of identification to explain the likeness in behavior. The child was not imitating a single act; instead he was acting as if he were the same as—or like—the parent as an individual.

The likeness to what I said of the child actor is plain. But here the child is playing in earnest; he is not so much acting as edging his way into the man that he will become. In the idiom of the theater, he is a method actor, and this makes one of the pleasures we get from watching him—that he is being *us*. And an added pleasure here is that at the same time he is us as we once were. In watching him, we live our promise again, and are proud of seeing it repeated in him; for a moment, he makes us believe that that fulfills it.

The grown member of a culture (ours or a simpler one) no longer acts a part. Yet he has models as the child did, by which he directs his conduct and which mold his personality. In a simple society, the models are few: there are a few traditional trades and offices, their places are firmly marked in the culture, and the man who follows one slips into the character that clothes it. He is indeed like a character in a folk tale—the king's jester, or the village cobbler, or the miller with a golden thumb. The whole outline of his personality has been drawn for him like a contour map when his society fixed his place.

A man in such a society is not aping another living man. He conforms to and thinks himself into a more general model of what he should be. He knows by tradition what is expected of those who fill each post in his culture. There is an accepted picture of the ideal man in his post, and this is the picture to which he looks up and with which he identifies himself.

A complex culture does not have such clearcut pictures for its members. Here a man's function does not fix his outline: there are no single models for the jester and the miller. A man's job may still be simple, but his place is not, because it is not fixed only by what he does for a living. His society now has many groups, some of which overlap in him; and each group to which he belongs creates another place for him. His character is a complex of all the traits which carry him into each of his groups in turn.

A dozen groups and more cross at every place in our culture: the Freemasons and the poker school, the trade union and the family, the P.T.A. and the Pennsylvania Dutch. The same man belongs to many different groups, whose demands are not at all one. And he can keep his loyalties to all, their conflict perpetually unresolved and perpetually in balance, because he can identify himself in turn with the model member of each. A full and many-sided modern society draws its strength from this criss-cross of different loyalties.

6

Yet the full and many-sided society pays a price for the multitude of its loyalties. Each of them fosters its own set of values, and we have failed so far to knit these into one set. Not that we have tried very hard: our failure springs from habit and prejudice more often than from a conflict of values. For example, our society pays lip service to the value of scientific evidence, but cannot persuade people by any show of statistics that the death penalty does not discourage murder. This is not because murder outrages their humanity, but on the contrary because it throws doubt on it. They catch in themselves the gales of rage, the hatred of a nagging mate, and the soft urge to poison a rival; and their revulsion for the murderer is also their fear of that glimpse in the dark mirror.

Here is the leading edge of panic in modern man which drags his society after him. It is his failure to make a unity of, as it were to make head or tail of, two sets of values. On one side, he is taught to take as his own a ragbag of secondhand traditions about human motives that are out of date. And on the other, he is harried to treat as gospel (a new gospel) the newsworthy speculations of scientists whose context he does not know. No wonder that he listens to them with the mulish suspicion of a jury hearing the expert evidence of cranks at the trial of a psychopath.

This double vision of the conscience will not be cured by adding a rapid course in biology to the school curriculum. It has been natural in the debate around the Two Cultures to treat the division between them as an issue in education; but it has been a fault, and I confess my share in it. This has made it seem that science and lit-

erature are bundles of information, and that all we need
do is to swop them about more.

But we shall not mend the rivalry of cultures by turning them into compulsory courses at school. After all,
arithmetic has been taught there for as long as reading
has, without leaving a trace of mathematical curiosity in
those who turn with pleasure to books. What divides the
cultures is not the insulation of information but of sympathy. They are not, even now, two separate claimants
for educational time, but for understanding. The problem
is not to get science and literature equally into the public's head, but jointly into the public mind and outlook.

It is not accidental that western man, with his strong
sense of individual personality, expresses himself in science and literature together. The one is not a technique
and the other is not an entertainment, and neither is a
bundle of information. They fix two modes of knowledge
which are complementary, and which necessarily flourish
and wither together. Seen in this way, the breach between them is not merely a gap in contemporary education, but is the visible sign of a loss of confidence in the
identity of man.

These essays have shown it is possible to create again
a coherent philosophy of man, and that not by denying
but by accepting the relevance of modern science. And
neither must we deny the relevance of art (of modern
art) which, for simplicity, I have illustrated in literature.
Lord Cherwell used to recount that the wife of the Warden of All Souls said to him when he was a young professor of physics at Oxford, 'My husband says that a man
who has got a First in Greats could get up science in a
fortnight.' The Warden of All Souls must have been a silly
man; but so is the young professor of physics (I meet
him from time to time) who thinks that any good scientist could get up culture in a fortnight.

Art and science are the manmade monuments in which
our past culture is fixed, and they are also the sensitive

probes which signal the direction of its future. Meanwhile, the broad and present culture of the everyday tries dispiritedly to think where to put modern science—and, for that matter, modern art. It grumbles that science has disrupted morality, because it has freed human behavior from the ancient sanctions of fear and conformity. And it protests that the arts are equally scandalous, because the women do not have the look of Renoir and the manners of Oscar Wilde that scandalized our grandparents yesterday.

7

The virtues and vices that the characters in literature display are as familiar to us as our own. They are our own; they come directly from the world that sits facing us behind the white page, waiting for us to shut the book. The Vicar of Wakefield is kindly, Doctor Zhivago is in love, Cressida deceives, and the Idiot is compassionate. Perhaps their actions at times are rather larger than life: Mark Antony is infatuated on a regal scale, and Samson Agonistes is more than commonly heroic. But the mold of their virtues and vices is our own, and almost everything that they do by way of sacrifice or outrage can be matched in the columns of the Sunday paper.

Yet the force of their examples is different from that of the Sunday gossip. There is no secret about that. We simply have their stories in more detail. But to put the difference so simply is too transparent, and overlooks more than it sees. It is not the bulk of detail that distinguishes the work of literature, but its kind. More columns would tell you more about the Sunday love match, but they would not bring it to life: they would not bring it into your life. The love affairs of literature enter your life because they are told with the kind of detail which you live in love. Literature does not present them passively as stories, but with the active detail of inner experience.

I have already discussed at length the conflicts in that experience. Now I am concerned with something else: the fact that it is active. This is what makes it a part of your own life, and puts it solidly into the context of the everyday. The virtues and vices that struggle in books would be as abstract as they are in *The Faerie Queene* and *The Pilgrim's Progress* if you were not engaged in the action concretely, as you are in writing a love letter. A poem or a novel is not a sermon; it does not preach about values, it sets them at odds; and they have a meaning for you only if you feel the action as your own. Only then can these values confront and influence the values and the actions in your daily life.

But if this is true of the virtues and vices that are entangled in books, it must also be true of those that are paraded in sermons. The fact is that we are no longer a simple culture that can be instructed by sermons. We are not bound by commandments but by loyalties, and we have more loyalties than can be covered by fiat. We have to weigh their conflicting values for ourselves, on this occasion and on that, once in this favor and once in that, in the natural day to day of our conduct. In a complex and many-sided culture, we have to develop our ethic in our own actions, now within one group and now within another. Perhaps this group or that may have a book of rules for its members, but there can be no book to balance for any one of us, once for all, the loyalties that bind him to a dozen groups.

Indeed, at bottom, no code of ethics can be or has been a book of rules, now or in the past. A book of rules can dictate what is fair but not what is sporting; it can tell you formally how to play a game, but it cannot tell you how to behave in it. The ethic of the game, the standard of conduct of those who are devoted to it, is expressed in phrases that do not stand in the rules: 'play

the game', 'play ball', 'that's not cricket', 'act like a gentleman'. Such phrases and such thoughts contain but do
not define the ambiguous concepts which truly characterize the game. And the niceties of social conduct are
more like a game than an army drill. We can write and
rewrite the regulations and the lawbooks, but we cannot
define and we cannot impose by edict the values which
truly make up our ethic. They are not written out but
acted out.

8

The values which are acted out in literature of course
cover the whole spectrum. Almost every virtue is engaged, for example, in *The Merchant of Venice*, of all
plays. Nevertheless, it can be roughly said that literature
is most often engaged with the values that center in the
feelings of one person for another. These are, so to speak,
the intimate values; they act at close quarters and at first
hand; the message that they carry is specific, from me to
you. The most masterful of these values is love, and we
may take it for the pattern of them all.

Yet when we reflect, it is not the intimacy of love that
characterizes it and the values allied to it. They have a
deeper sense in common—all of them, in the whole range
from tenderness to compassion, and from generosity to
respect and friendship. Through all of them there runs
the double sense of devotion by me, and sympathy for
you.

It is crucial that we should recognize the two strands
in all these values. A feeling that goes out from one person and ends at another has two elements. There is, as it
were, the commitment at my end: the sense of devotion.
And coupled with it there is what moves and directs my
devotion, what my devotion finds: a sympathy for you.

They are the giving and the gift, and neither is whole without the other.

If this is so, then it follows that I the giver need the gift as much as you do. Simple devotion is not enough for me: I need to feel sympathy for you to guide it and to charge it with meaning. The object of my devotion must not merely enslave me; it must fulfill and fill out my self, and I must feel that I have become more by finding something that I lacked. Passion and affection, kindness and pity, do not go out into the empty air to seek an object of devotion, whatever it is. They seek on my behalf another self which engages my sympathy because it fulfills my self.

9

This analysis explains why in the end I can be engaged with equal devotion by abstract sympathies. For there are other means of fulfillment than private relations. A man can find or make ideal models which personify what he wants to be, or to be in part. In a complex society, there are many groups that present such models to him. Devotion and sympathy are now entwined for him in less intimate values: duty and loyalty, grandeur and sacrifice and the rest of those social virtues that ask no questions.

What can keep the social values in balance, one set of them against another, when they command whole populations? Edith Cavell, facing a firing squad, said 'Patriotism is not enough'. No loyalty is enough, no bright sense of mission, no righteous conviction that our opponents are not merely wrong but perversely wrong—they really know better. A nation cannot be run that way, and the world cannot. We cannot personify states as if they were men, and have them treat their rivalries as if they were love affairs. Social life cannot be ruled by an elaboration of the values that derive from devotion and sympathy.

There must be other values than these intimate ones, and of course there are. Love is not the only pattern of virtue, and hate is not the only vice. There is another set of virtues, which is founded on the central value of truth, and which is denied when truth is denied. But there is this disparity: that in our culture, truth does not command the passionate assent that the intimate values do. We live by human links, and it matters more to us that others share our beliefs than that they be true. So somehow falsehood (and even deception) does not have the personal air of outrage that, say, disloyalty has; perhaps, we say, it is only an error. We are willing to treat a lie in private life as an act of kindness, and in public life as an act of policy.

The values that derive from truth are as old as our civilization. But they have been less critical in the past than they are now because there was not then a strong body of formal knowledge to set an example of truth. We have now seen science in search of truth give us an immense command in the affairs of nature, and we wonder whether we are wise to go on slighting it in our affairs of state. This is the uneasiness that haunts us whenever we dismiss the ethical implications of science.

10

Truth is not the monopoly of science, and the values that derive from truth were known before the Scientific Revolution. Nevertheless, I shall base my derivation of these values on the practice of science. My reason is twofold. This procedure shows most clearly how we form an ethic by acting it. And it shows how practical these values are, if we are willing to use them. I have followed the same method before in *Science and Human Values* and I shall do no more now than sketch it.

It is commonly said that science is ethically neutral,

because its discoveries can be used for good or ill. This judgment confuses two meanings of the word *science:* the process of discovery, and what is discovered at the end of it. Of course what is discovered is neutral, whether it is Hooke's law, or a semiconductor, or the theory of evolution. But the long and dedicated activity of the men who made these discoveries was not neutral: it was firmly directed and strictly judged.

In practicing science, we accept from the outset an end which is laid down for us. The end of science is to discover what is true about the world. The activity of science is directed to seek the truth, and it is judged by that criterion. We can practice science only if we value the truth.

Truth is an individual value, which dictates the conduct of a scientist alone with his work. It becomes a source of social values only when a society accepts the assumption that no belief will survive if it conflicts with what is true. This is the unspoken assumption which the society of scientists as a body makes. They agree that the discovery of truth is an end in itself, not only for each scientist but for the culture of science. It follows that a whole nexus of social values can be deduced from the single injunction that the culture of science has a common duty to seek the truth.

Of course, this assumes that the truth has not already been found (and indeed that it is not there to be found, once for all, like a lost umbrella). A society which believes that the truth needs no more seeking is authoritarian. By contrast, the society of scientists must be organized to evolve step by step in the discovery of truth. Therefore the single scientist must value originality of mind and independence of character, and the culture as a whole must safeguard them by placing a value on dissent. And dissent in turn must be protected by justice and by freedom—freedom of thought, of speech and writing, of movement and assembly. We must not take these for granted, simply because lip service to them has become hackneyed, as if they were self-evident and natural values in any society. Plato did not offer freedom of speech and writing in his Republic; and he did not offer justice to those who demanded them, but exile. Freedom is valued in a culture that wants to encourage dissent and to stimulate originality and independence. It belongs to a society which is open to change, and which esteems the agent of change, the individual, above its own peace of mind.

So far I have derived from the conditions for the practice of science only those values which make for change. But a culture must also have values which resist change. In engineering terms, it must have a certain inertia, by which it maintains what it holds to be true now, and makes the truth of tomorrow fight for life. In order to be stable, the culture of science must give honor to those whose work is superseded as well as to the newcomer. It must treat the truth of the past, and the way it was found, with dignity. It must respect the man's way of working more than what he finds, because the process of discovery is more important to it than any discovery.

In this sense, respect is a central value in the culture of science. The old and the new are linked by respect for each man and his work, not as an achievement but as an example, a shining way of working. This is the true meaning of progress in science: that the past is respected in the present, Newton in Einstein, Arab arithmetic in the computer, and the waterwheel in the dynamo. Progress is not a graveyard of the obsolete but a living history.

Respect is in some ways a personal value, the social expression of which is tolerance. Tolerance is a modern value, because it is a necessary condition for the coherence of a complex society in which different men have different views. And tolerance in this setting is not a negative value; it must grow out of an active respect for others. It is not enough in science or in modern society

to agree that other men are entitled to their opinions.
We must believe that the opinions of others are interesting in themselves, and deserve our respect even when we
think them wrong. In science and in modern life, to be
wrong may be tragic, but it is not wicked.

11

A just ethic must be grounded in a single-minded philosophy. And that must grasp, I have shown, that the
identity of man derives from the coming together of two
modes of experience, and is fixed in two modes of knowledge: knowledge of the physical world, and knowledge
of the self. We cannot hope to make a modern structure
of values which belittles either mode. A soundly based
ethic begins in the action of understanding both nature
and man. And scientific understanding is part of that: the
choice between good and evil must not fly in the face
of the choice between true and false.

But, of course, the matter goes deeper than that. What
the scientific mode has to teach the conscience is the
code of values of science, which makes the pursuit of
truth its first endeavor and an end in itself. Nothing
erodes the public morality so much as the acquiescence
in what is expedient when what is true is unpalatable.

If this were all that could be said, we should indeed
be in a hopeless state. Telling the truth on matters of fact
is a laudable rule, and the success of science is built on
this simple base. But if this were all the content of science, it would be an arid study; and if it were all that it
had to say about the conduct of our lives, it would leave
us quite lopsided. We should have one master rule, and
one rule only, in all matters which can be put to the test
of fact. And we should be back with the old hugger-
mugger of loyalties in all those thousand issues of daily

life, private and public, which cannot be put to practical test.

And of course this is the picture that the public at large has of its own perplexity. The only conception of science that it has is an impersonal machinery for grinding out the factual truth. If a question has an answer, then the machine will give it, and there will be only one answer to each question. So the progress of science becomes a conquest by the machine of one field after another in which a man used to be his own master. The man who longs to be a person believes that the truths of science come day by day to pin him down, a pin for this joint and a pin for that bone, until he will become an articulated mechanism of facts. In these terms, he knows very well that he is losing the tug of war for his personality.

Alas, he is right. If the struggle of civilized man for a coherent self is fought on these grounds, it will certainly be lost. Nor will it matter much that the authoritarian faith to come will then be scientific; it would be just as authoritarian and as disastrous if it were anti-scientific—Germany showed that in 1933. If we have nothing to offer civilized man except truth to fact on the one side, and blind loyalty on the other, he is lost: there is no place for a personal self on either side.

The values that truly engage our lives are not such barren rules. In particular, the ethic of science does not end at truth to fact, and indeed cannot be derived from that naïve meaning of truth. It is truth as knowledge, the endless pursuit, that generates the values of science as I have derived them. And it is the self as knowledge, the expanding reach, that confronts these values and has to find a common aspiration with them.

12

What have the Puritan values of science in common with the intimate values that the arts echo from our private lives? Is there anything that can bind truth and justice, independence and dissent in science to the warmer values in which devotion and sympathy are entwined—to love and generosity, tenderness and compassion? Or must we accept that the formal machinery in which science is presented encloses its values, and keeps them apart from the longings in which men seek for their fulfillment?

In the light of what I have argued, the form of the last sentence itself makes it plain that there cannot be such a rigid exclusion. True, at any moment science exists as a closed body of knowledge, and can be provisionally presented on machines. But it had to be invented, and it will have to be enlarged, not by machines but by men. And the imagination that drives these men, the greed for new experience and the search in it for new likenesses with the old, is of a piece with that of the poet and of any one of us who looks to round out his self beyond himself. The values of science are generated by the search and not by the findings, and it would be extraordinary if they turned out to match the character of a machine that can only record the findings.

So when we look closely at the list of values that I have traced in science, it is not a surprise to find some that are also listed among the intimate values. One such double value is tolerance, and another is respect. They are the bridge between the two sets of values; and they are in effect one bridge and not two, because they are related values. As I have presented them, tolerance and respect form a pair of values, each of which supports the other; and they are linked together, whether we look at them in the list of scientific values or of intimate values. Twelve years ago I wrote,

> Tolerance among scientists cannot be based on indifference, it must be based on respect.

In the same sense, and only in the same sense, as an active relation, tolerance also has a place among the intimate values.

The crucial concept of the pair is respect. For respect is a value common to both lists, and yet does not have quite the same meaning in each. In science, respect goes out from me to you: I respect your work although I would not do it that way, I respect your approach although I do not share it. I respect you as a person who has earned the right to work as he chooses, but the deepest thing that I have learned from you is to guard my own right.

This is not the more intimate meaning of respect. I respect Jonathan Swift in some of these ways, of course (otherwise it would be wrong to use the same word), but I also feel more warmly; I do not think of him as a different person from me. Perhaps I respect him most for what is in me and will never come out: the extravagances, the grievances, the scurrilous poems, the hidden offhand tenderness—all that hatred of himself in which he fiercely fixed his compassion for man. I could not respect myself if I did not respect Swift.

Here is the point at which the values of science and self meet and complement one another; and it does not matter whether we call that tight complex of common values tolerance or respect or human dignity. In all of them, science seeks the dignity of the work, and we as men seek the dignity of man. And we seek that not as a discovery outside ourselves but in ourselves. My respect for Jonathan Swift is self-respect; I add to his achievement my sense of identity with his humanity. In this conjunction between the work and the man, between nature and the self, science and literature give a dignity to our culture which is larger than either, in an ethic that unites respect for what is done with respect for what we are.

Every ethic looks two ways: it has a public face and a private one. That is, it must hold a man within his society, and yet it must make him feel that he follows his own free bent. No ethic is effective which does not link both these, the social duty with the sense of individuality. In this respect above all we have failed to make science part of our ethic; for we have allowed it to be pictured as a body of public knowledge and no more. As a result, we have left it to the arts to carry the private conscience that we no longer accept by edict. I have shown that neither picture is fair. Science carries its core of personal imagination too, and the knowledge of self that the arts foster reaches out to the selves of others from our own. What joins the two cultures and fuses them into one ethic is this double sense: the private respect for the accomplished work, the public tolerance for another man's thoughts and passions. Their conjunction is the sense of human dignity which sustains each man freely within his society, and makes him the unique and double creature: man, the social solitary.

13

I called these essays *The Identity of Man* because I wanted to unravel the two halves of that, the machine from the self. Man is a machine by birth but a self by experience. And the special character of the self lies in its experience not of nature but of others. A man enters the lives of other men more directly than he can enter nature, because he recognizes his own thoughts and feelings in them; he learns to make theirs his own, and to find in himself a deeper self that has the features of all humanity. The knowledge of nature teaches him to act, and makes him master of the creation. The knowledge of self does not teach him to act but to be; it steeps him in the human predicament and the predicament of life; it makes him one with all the creatures.

It is the tragedy of our age that we fear the machine in man, though it is as noble as the self; and we have grown to doubt whether it will leave us a self. We will not believe that what the machine learns and teaches, a knowledge of science, can strengthen our ethic, which now languishes among our random loyalties. Yet the search for knowledge in nature generates values as rich as we get by reaching for the knowledge of self. When we pursue knowledge for action we learn (among other things) a special respect for a man's work. And when we look into another man for knowledge of our selves, we learn a more intimate respect for him as a man. Our pride in man and nature together, in the nature of man, grows by this junction into a single sense: the sense of human dignity. The ethics of science and of self are linked in this value, and more than all our partial loyalties it gives a place and a hope to the universal identity of man.

Dr. J. Bronowski, who is now Deputy Director and Fellow of The Salk Institute for Biological Studies in La Jolla, California, is a mathematician, statistician, teacher, inventor, administrator, poet, historian, literary critic, and philosopher of science. Born in Poland in 1908, he was educated in English schools and at Cambridge University. During World War II, Dr. Bronowski was a pioneer in the development of operations research methods and, as Scientific Deputy to the British Chiefs of Staff Mission to Japan in 1945, he wrote the British report "The Effects of the Atomic Bombs at Hiroshima and Nagasaki."

From 1945 to 1950, Dr. Bronowski led research for the British Government in applying statistical methods to the economics of industry. From 1950 until 1964, he was Director of Research of the National Coal Board in Great Britain. In 1953, he was Carnegie Visiting Professor at the Massachusetts Institute of Technology, where he delivered a series of lectures that initiated the discussion of the "two cultures" and later were published in the widely read book *Science and Human Values*. In addition, Dr. Bronowski has written three books on literature *The Poet's Defence*, *The Face of Violence*, and *William Blake and the Age of Revolution*, and two books on intellectual history *The Common Sense of Science* and (with Professor Bruce Mazlish) *The Western Intellectual Tradition*.